Translated and Edited by Frances and Sidney Alexander

THE
BERENSON
COLLECTION

Preface by Nicky Mariano

Introduction and Catalogue by Franco Russoli

ARTI GRAFICHE RICORDI - MILANO

Published under the auspices of the Italian commission for UNESCO and
the national commission for UNESCO of the United States of America

"*I TATTI*"

THE BERENSON COLLECTION

Bernard Berenson was
born in Lithuania & taken
to Boston at the age of ten.
There he remained till he
graduated at Harvard with
~~the class of~~ 1887.

In the 12 years passed unin-
terruptedly in the States he
became a devoted Bostonian,
New Englander, & American.
After sixty years ~~for the~~
most part spent in Europe
~~the~~ his love for the land
~~his~~ ~~feeling~~ ~~for America~~
~~of~~ his & the people who
~~has not~~
~~had been~~ so kind to him
during his formative
years has increased
rather than diminished

May 17, 52

W. Rothenstein: *B. Berenson*

PREFACE

*M*any years ago, at Villa Gattaia, while wandering about with its owner Carlo Loeser from one room to the other, I noticed that a small Quattrocento panel, belonging to the School of the Marches, was no longer in its place. I asked Loeser whether it was being restored. «No», he said, « I was fed up with it and gave it back to the man who sold it to me. I have not yet made up my mind about what to take in exchange for it. This business of bartering is great fun, the greatest fun for all of us collectors. Even if, in discarding one object, while hoping to get a better one in exchange, we sometimes make colossal blunders. I am sure that Bernard Berenson too, perhaps more cautiously than the rest of us, loves to play the same game». When I answered that in all the time I had so far spent at I Tatti, not one object of art, not one picture, not one piece of furniture had changed its place, I saw clearly from his expression that he did not believe a word of what I had been saying. So Bernard Berenson is not a real collector, I thought on my way home. He does not share the dominating passion of his colleagues. An object once appreciated, chosen and put in its place acquires for him an almost sentimental value, perhaps connected with the recollection of how and where he first saw it. Then what is Bernard Berenson? An amateur and, at the same time, a keeper in the real sense of the word, who does not admit that a harmony once created should be disturbed by a capricious and childish desire for novelty. In his «SKETCH FOR A SELF-PORTRAIT», written in 1941, describing his house, he says: «...These hangings, these paintings, these art objects were not acquired first and foremost with an eye to making a collec-tion, but almost exclusively to adorn my abode. When that was completed some thirty years ago I stopped buying. Indeed I have always disclaimed being a collector ».[1]

How many times we have tried to persuade him that the Madonna and Angels by Lippo Memmi (plate XIII) should be placed in a better light. We went so far as to put it where we thought it should be during one of his absences, hoping that on his return he would accept the innovation as a pleasant surprise. No sooner had he noticed the change than he sternly ordered us to put it back in its accustomed place. When I objected that it should be seen from farther away, he said that it had been in all probability ordered for a small chapel and was therefore intended to be looked at from close at hand.

He was unwilling to part even from two forgeries. One of them, a Madonna and Child, vaguely trecento-like in style is the first picture he ever bought and judging from an old photo of his

(1) Pantheon books edition p. 167.

15

study, in which it is clearly discernible in a place of honour, he must have been taken in by it for a number of years. Later on it was relegated to the second floor, but he liked it to be in the house and to remind him occasionally of his youthful incompetence. The other one, a Madonna and Angels in the style of Botticelli he kept in his study although half hidden away, as it amused him to look at it from time to time. He told me that having bought it, he went on believing in its authenticity only for a few hours. Both these forgeries are probably products of Joni's studio.

Berenson was almost indifferent to the name one might give to his own pictures. For years he went on attributing the Madonna from the Panciatichi collection (plate XXXIV) to Baldovinetti, *while all his colleagues were already at one in considering her one of the finest works of Domenico Veneziano. The small Deposition (plate II) generally attributed to Giotto appeared in the last editions of his Lists as the work of an immediate follower. Intense enjoyment was what he wanted above all. The ambition of increasing the value of his collection by high-sounding attributions was not in him. Already the word « collection » annoyed him and we carefully hid from him the small catalogues prepared for the benefit of visitors in each room. He refused to admit that, attracted by his name and reputation, visitors in ever increasing numbers, especially American ones, would flock to I Tatti. Woe to me if I had to tell him that a letter of introduction had been presented by people who were spending only two days in Florence. It made him quite angry. « How much time will they give to Florence and its priceless treasures? » he would say. Several years ago I asked him to write a short biographical note of himself, which I might give to the many people who asked for it. When he handed it to me I was surprised to find that his collection was not even mentioned in it.*[1]

It is another proof of Berenson's tendency to consider the works of art at I Tatti in the first

(1) The first page of this biographical note is reproduced in facsimile.

place as furnishing and explains why so little is known of their provenance. He did not share the ambition of Chinese collectors who take the greatest pride in the huge seals of former collectors on their possessions. Perhaps Berenson was first and foremost an artist and then only an art historian and critic. His immediate almost physical reaction to the work of art explains the considerable influence he has exercised in epochs of discovery, when a style formerly neglected or totally unknown was taken up and appreciated and the difference between great works of art and minor ones had to be discussed and established. That is what happened with the early Sienese School of painting at the end of the century and with the first shiploads of Chinese art that reached Europe after the Boxer Rebellion in 1900. Chinese painting, especially, was an absolute revelation at that moment for European connoisseurs, while in the United States it was already represented in several public and private collections.

During our numerous journeys I have seen Berenson passionately dedicated to a given type of art, Egyptian or Classical or Byzantine or Carolingian or Fatimide, not to speak of the Schools of painting in other European countries. With each of them he wanted to get thoroughly acquainted. I have seen him enraptured before the archaic group at Calchis, before the frescoes from the grottoes of Turfan in the Museum of Berlin, before the wooden sculptures of the Oseberg Ship in Oslo. I have heard him discuss problems of style and date with the students specialized each in his own branch, as if nothing else existed for him at that moment. I remember a famous Egypt-ologist dumbfounded when, in one of the tombs of the Nobles, he heard Bernard Berenson speak of the freshness and intensity of colour of the hieroglyphs. The learned interpreter of these ideograms had never noticed their colour.

As the years went by his sense of property kept fading away. In his diary he wrote on May 30th 1947:

« Walked in my own garden. My own? What am I saying? I have little if any sense of property and least of all with regard to what I own here. A bit more perhaps in regard to my American investments, possibly because they are so abstract. Here I enjoy house, pictures, books, garden, fields, knowing that they cannot be immediately snatched away from me but that they are only temporarily mine — verliehen — like a prized decoration in Prussia. Perhaps if I had inherited my possessions I might feel differently, but twice uprooted, first from Lithuania to the United States and from there to Italy, how can I feel the fixity of possessions? ».

When in the spring of 1956 our friend and neighbour Roberto Papini proposed to Bernard Berenson that he should entrust the publication of this volume to the Officine Grafiche Ricordi he did not get a ready response. Bernard Berenson said that he would prefer any activity of that kind to be taken up when he would no longer be of this world. Roberto Papini did not give in and being a magician of words ended by persuading him. Most of the preparatory work for the illustrations was done in the summer of 1956 but in 1957 Roberto Papini's premature death brought everything to a standstill. Thus Bernard Berenson's original wish that the book should not appear during his lifetime has been fulfilled. Yet I feel sure, knowing how much he approved of the samples of illustrations he was able to look at, that were he still among us he could not but be pleased to see the work completed in such a satisfactory manner. Therefore I have no hesitation in expressing my gratitude in the name of Bernard Berenson to the direction and the technicians of the Officine Grafiche Ricordi for the way in which the work has been carried out, as well as to Franco Russoli for having followed Bernard Berenson's instructions in the handling of catalogue and introduction. Finally, I want to thank the President and Fellows of Harvard University for having given their consent to the publication of this volume.

NICKY MARIANO

San Martino a Mensola, June 12, 1960

INTRODUCTION

"*My house, I trust, expresses my needs, my tastes and aspirations.*" Thus begin the celebrated pages of a "Sketch for a Self-Portrait" in which Bernard Berenson speaks of the criteria underlying the creation of I Tatti: a house which not only responds to the spiritual and physical needs of the man who lived in it ("... an interior that suited my muscular and respiratory ideations with regard to space and my eyes with regard to shapes and colours") but which is really a *portrait*, an objective projection of Bernard Berenson's personality. Hence, the dwelling acquires an autonomy, an originality, so that even its creator could contemplate it "like a beautiful object in nature or art which one does not dream of possessing, and not as an appendix to one's own ego." Characteristically, with simple elegance, Berenson gives us the key with which to enter his house and understand his spirit. Here we find an unusual combination of austerity and refinement, of stimulation and relaxation. For these qualities, seemingly contrary, were integrated in Berenson's sense of life. His egocentricity consisted, primarily, in an examination of conscience, a lust to know, a desire for critical rapport with the world, a drive towards perfection. And yet these absolutes were always balanced by the mellow wisdom which understands if it does not condone, ever conscious of the eternal relationship between absolute and relative, universal and personal. Sharp-eyed psychological awareness tempered mystical and mythical impulses; an ethical conception of history always rendered his judgment practical and current. If he did not suffer fools easily, if he was ironic, or affirmed principles and respect for rules — all this testified to an inexorable quest for ideals. On the other hand, his restlessness, his discontent, his conviction of not having fulfilled himself testified to the same quest. To objectify his intuition of the absolute, to choose a place which might serve as a symbol of the essential harmony between man and nature, to cull the fruits of man's knowledge (books) and man's creative intuitions (works of art) — this, it seems to me, Berenson achieved at I Tatti. The limpid sweetness of these hills, the woods and gardens and orchards sloping towards the city, the tonal passages from greens to greys to ochres, the friendly fusion of nature and the works of man create a sense of confidence in reality, and at the same time, set us wondering as to the origins of such an enchanting harmony. Because of its extraordinary grace and exceptional beauty, that which might seem a refuge or an oasis reveals itself instead as an outpost for speculation, goading us to eternal questions. It is perfectly understandable that this chosen spot should correspond to that idea of the "perfect" which shaped a humanist educated in the tradition of English thought of the second half of the nineteenth century. All the components of an aristocracy of genius had fermented in an atmosphere, rarified and passionate at the same time. One must not avoid any fatigue or any risk in order that, subsequently, one might make clear-minded choices and rejections. One must limit the radius of action of one's ego to achieve a wiser and deeper range. Clearly this is not an easy "dandyism" but one which must be endured. Instead of adjusting to preconceived norms, this is a "dandyism" of continuous struggle. It was impossible to accept tastes, attitudes, modes of living already codified, whether by the mass or by the élite. Rather, it was necessary to find oneself alone with oneself, with one's environment, with Nature. And always to be in control, always aware of one's own strength and weakness, always at the mirror — accepting the colloquy. Thus, symbolism and pragmatism, ethics and hedonism were combined: thus, the mystic aspiration to arrive at the vital core of being, beyond every phenomenological reference, had to be verified in every daily action.

But this quest might also be recognized and reconstituted in any historical epoch. By analogy, any civilization might lend itself as a term of reference. Histories might be recovered and clarified as patterns of current situations — for example, in the art, poetry, thought of the ancient Far East, or of the Middle Ages or of the Italian Renaissance. The main lines of speculation however, are clear: a taste which is pre-Raphaelite, Symbolist, intimate, in that order. Rather than taking formalistic and aestheticising positions, Berenson posed psychological problems and examined social motivations. Rather than dealing with works as indeterminately beautiful, expressions of an a-historical and extra-temporal absolute, the goal was to interprete according to present conditions and knowledge and personal principles. The esthetic moment, the mystic vision, were indissolubly bound up with an ethical and civic function. Hence, the choice of Settignano as the site for his home should be considered in part determined by these ideals of Berenson's youth. For in Settignano one finds, indeed, that union of nature and the works of man, mystical rapture in the All and rational serenity, ascetic purity and exquisite refinement. A Franciscan place, contemplative in an oriental sense; at the same time, a place rich with history and passions: the point of encounter of ecstacy and vigilant criticism. Nature here is, above all, tamed, cultivated, not at all exotic, possessing perhaps more than elsewhere, a virginal sincerity, an intangible freedom, a power of continually suggesting a sense of the absolute. The mirror, hence, of man truly made free by his knowledge, his feeling and his discipline. It is no wonder, therefore, that the Florentine hills were the favourite spot for cultivated British, Americans, and Germans, enamoured of the Primitives seen through the eyes of Ruskin or Pater, or of neo-Platonic thought and life at the Medicean court. For Berenson, however, this locality, must have sounded more secret springs of his temperament and touched on reasons and motives inspiring his work and thought. Thus was born the villa of I Tatti, and it developed, took shape, acquired ever more form and character corresponding to the body and soul of the master of the place. Another writer might have spoken of the life at I Tatti — recreating the serene, yet surprising, atmosphere, the fusion of work and contemplation, of solitude and everstimulating conversation, which have made the story and legend of Berenson's house. I certainly cannot substitute for Roberto Papini, friend and associate, who with affectionate insistence convinced Bernard Berenson to permit this book, which Papini had so thoughtfully prepared. And I must also ask pardon of other friends who have savoured of long-intimate visits to I Tatti for this too-extended introduction to that which should have been my only task: to list and comment in the collector's own words on the paintings which Berenson chose to "adorn" his abode. "Indeed I have always disclaimed being a collector." In fact it was never Berenson's aim to become the proud possessor of rare works, of masterpieces of illustrious personalities. Nor did he want to form an organic collection of painting, sculpture, art objects which might document the activity of certain masters or the development of a school. He acquired works, which — prized above all for their intrinsic esthetic qualities, or for their importance in the field of culture and studies — had value with reference to his spiritual exigencies, his life. Again, an attitude which reveals the mixture of egocentricity and true humility composing Berenson's personality. He wanted works, not to make a show of them, or to catalogue them scientifically; but rather that they might become part of his very existence. Some of these works were to help excite him to life; others were only to serve as elements in a serene composition around him, visual points of imaginative repose. Alongside masterpieces by great artists, stimulating and demanding guests, the "minor" works were to form a more affable daily companionship, always lively and precious because they were "good to live with". He also wanted to have always near him witnesses of those worlds which had most fascinated his imagination and thought — the Orient, for example, and the Italian Renaissance. Hence, the bronze sacred cat of Egypt, (tutelary deity) the Chinese paintings, reliefs, terra-cottas, the Persian miniatures; and, in the library and spacious rooms, Buddha heads, austere yet florid, so conducive to conversation and study. Resting on shelves and on Renaissance furniture are the small gold-backgrounded panels and everywhere, paintings lined up on the staircase and along the halls and corridors whose windows open out upon the harmonious gardens. Set under the great Franciscan tryptich of Sassetta are two heads of Buddhist divinities which seem, indeed, to recall the pages which Berenson wrote in 1903 on the affinity between Sienese and Far Eastern art. Occasional works which are or were in the house (such as a Matisse landscape given by Berenson to Prince Paul of Yugoslavia for the Belgrade Museum) testify to the collector's wide-flung cultural interests, moments in his life, affections, friendships. For instance, a ceramic by Picasso, a composition by Guttuso, evoke Berenson's frequently-opposed, polemical, always-alive judgment on various tendencies in modern and contemporary art.

We can, therefore, understand the true meaning of Berenson's words "... these hangings, paintings, these art objects were not acquired first and foremost with an eye to making a collection, but almost exclusively to adorn my abode. When that was completed some thirty years ago I stopped buying".

Insofar as his dwelling was like the ideal involucre of his person, reflecting his "tastes, needs, aspirations", to furnish his house with art objects is the same as saying, to gather works of art expressing his interests as student and critic. It also meant bringing together those pictorial and sculptural statements, which, by their images and forms and colours, would create around him a coherent, serene, visual concept in harmony with his personality. Not a collection, therefore, determined by outward scientific or hedonistic norms, and even less so by the exhibition of his discoveries or findings as an "expert", but rather the continuation and complement, via *things*, of practical daily affairs, research, dreams, thoughts and emotions. That is to say, a collection conceived of as a Life. "Merely entering into Mr. Berenson's house... one is aware of the coherence with which saying and surrounding, environment and figure could be combined, that is, how his words and personality fused with the pictures, sculptures, furniture and other objects with which he loved to surround himself..." (Roberto Papi).

One would not dare *expertize* Berenson's pictures, especially not in his house. Not only would that be a ridiculous presumption, but an offense against the spirit with which these works were gathered together. In another place, on the occasion of special studies, such expertizing might be permissible, but not in this book which hopes to become part of his dwelling and wants only to make known those paintings which he had chosen, how and when he acquired them, the joy he took in judging them. This catalogue does not intend to serve the history of art so much as the history and comprehension of Berenson's personality. If the presentation and choice of his words and opinions be made so as faithfully to reflect the relationship between Berenson and his pictures, this work will necessarily make a contribution to the history of art criticism. Therefore, the bibliography relative to each painting of the collection, and my own observations, must be considered no more than a necessary appendix, in order to complete as fully as possible the history of the painting itself, considered here, however, essentially in so far as it figures in the I Tatti collection.

Berenson did not collect "minor" paintings simply for the pleasures of a sharp-eyed connoisseur. Rather, he found in such works some admirable qualities, "some singular and gracious eclecticism", an elegance and good taste, an example of Illustration and Decoration in a minor mode, fused with pleasant simplicity, which made them ideal life-companions, exquisite elements of "house furnishing".

Of many similar Florentine, Sienese, Umbrian, Ferrarese, Lombard and Venetian paintings he has never written; he has not included them in his *List of the Principal Artists and their Works*", although several of these works belong to centuries and schools of the Renaissance. In such cases, I have reported his judgments on the school in general to which he attributed the work. "It will be sufficient to make known my opinion", Mr. Berenson had advised me. Besides, his reluctance to write about the paintings in his possession is well known; also, his specific comments and illustrations are lacking for equally important works. Often, therefore, the change in attribution is documented only by diverse collocations of the painting in successive editions of the "List". Up to the last, I tried to find out from Berenson personally, or to dig out of his notes, his most recent attribution. Comparing it with the preceding, wherever changes existed, and collating it against the opinions of other scholars, new elements for the comprehension of his critical methods are made available. "It took the scattering of most private collections all over Europe to make me realize that mine was one of the best remaining". And not only, we might add, because of so many Italian masterpieces, especially the core of 14th and 15th century works which make his collection an indispensable anthology of early Sienese and early Florentine art, but especially because of the coherent spirit which informs it, the personality which it reflects. Even in the reproductions for this book subdivided approximately in chronological order, by school, Berenson's pictures remain secretly and intimately interconnected beyond any coldly scientific systematization. Now, in the settings determined by the master of the house, Harvard scholars will admire these works, and so will all those art lovers granted free access to I Tatti. Works of Giotto, Simone Martini, Lorenzetti, Sassetta, Gentile da Fabriano, Domenico Veneziano, Neroccio, Francesco di Giorgio, Matteo di Giovanni, Giovanni Bellini, Luca Signorelli, Vincenzo Foppa, Lorenzo Lotto — these are only a few names among the multitude whose works Berenson had collected and, as may be noted at once, in many cases, artists whom he had interpreted anew and whose poetry he had often rediscovered.

Works which summon up memories of peregrinations, youthful discoveries, long patient studies, enraptured insights and exhaustive research. And what masterpieces! Giotto is represented by a strong *Franciscan monk* which Berenson considers of the period of the Santa Croce frescoes, and by the sublime *Deposition* contemporary with the Peruzzi chapel frescoes — that is to say, by two distinct and basic moments for the understanding of Giotto's development. And the loftiest interpretation of his style in a new tonality is documented by the little "crucifixion" which Longhi has rejoined to the corpus of Stefano. Two tender saints, Lucy and Catherine, are examples of the sweetest and most delicate mood of Simone Martini, the mood which inspired the exquisite lyricism of the "Maestro of the Palazzo Venezia" and Lippo Memmi. And by Lippo Memmi himself, we find that masterpiece of spiritual and courteous poetic elegance, "the Virgin Enthroned", the lateral panels of which are in the Copenhagen museum.

The passionate tension of Pietro Lorenzetti's reliquary inevitably recalls the limpid sweetness of Ambrogio's Virgin, which now, by Berenson's generous gift, is in the Uffizi, flanking Saints Nicholas and Proculus which stood beside it in the altar painted for the church of S. Procolo. Giambono's St. Michael, central part of a polyptych dispersed among various collections and museums, is undoubtedly one of the culminations of this master's exuberant and fanciful art. But what can one add to the mere mention of Domenico Veneziano's *Panciatichi Madonna*, and of the three panels of the Franciscan polyptych painted by Sassetta for Borgo San Sepolcro? If these are fundamental pictures in the history of Italian art, neither can anyone who truly loves our paintings, ignore the works of Bernardo Daddi and Nardo di Cione, Lorenzo Monaco and Gentile da Fabriano and the enchanting series of Sienese panels from Sano di Pietro to Giovanni di Paolo, from the vibrant Francesco di Giorgio to the suave and diaphanous Neroccio di Bartolomeo, to the incisive Matteo di Giovanni. More naive and sentimental, perhaps, is the Umbrian grace of the Madonnas by Boccati and Bonfigli, while the fury, the "superhuman frenzy" of the Ferrarese masters may be found in the small panels which Berenson attributes to Ercole de' Roberti. Certainly it was easy for Berenson, Morelli's disciple and friend of Cagnola, Noseda and Frizzoni, to comprehend and love the melancholy and severe poetry of the Lombard masters, "the silvery trembling tones" of Foppa and Bergognone. And, of course, the man who proclaimed tactile values could not fail to possess an example of Luca Signorelli's austere art and powerful sense of form, and precisely in that genre wherein Signorelli's value as an illustrator most securely manifests itself — in the portrait. As for the Venetians, to whom Berenson dedicated his first Italian studies, it suffices to recall Giovanni Bellini's *Madonna* and Cima's *St. Sebastian* limpidly soaring in noonday light. The dramatic mysticism of Lorenzo Lotto's small Borromeo crucifixion would deserve a longer discussion in order to commemorate this master's poetic revelation so fundamentally revivified in Berenson's study.

Many other paintings in the collection are particularly interesting, with reference to the "Collector". For these are by unknown artists whose personalities and creative development Berenson was able to reconstruct by discovering linkages among works dispersed in the *mare magnum* of various attributions. Thus, we have Ugolino Lorenzetti's *Crucifixion* and a noble *Madonna* by the Master of the Castello Nativity — two of Berenson's most famous and vivid "creations". Other works remained anonymous even to him: restless, charming, unknown companions whose merits could be appreciated without unnecessarily unveiling the secrets of their origin.

Now all these treasures are entrusted to Berenson's two elective countries: the United States of America and Italy; more precisely to those two places where he was educated and where he lived: Harvard University and Florence. Saved from certain destruction and brought back from strange unsuitable places, these works live again in a friendly environment. Berenson valued the recognition of his collection not out of a Maecenas' vanity but because the gathering of it was one of his life aims and because, basically, it was a way of expressing his gratitude and love for others.

Thus, today, I Tatti — the first American institute for graduate studies in the history of Italian art, functioning in Italy — with its impressive collection of Italian master-pieces inseparable from Florence, continues in a double sense Berenson's labours for the benefit of our art.

It is difficult for me to express how grateful I am to Bernard Berenson for the faith which he demonstrated in entrusting me with this task. And I would also like to express my gratitude to Roberto Papini and my regret that I could not conduct the work in collaboration with him and under his guidance. A work which would have been much less successful — if indeed it could have been accomplished at all — without the invaluable and friendly assistance of Miss Nicky Mariano to whom I express my warmest thanks.

FRANCO RUSSOLI

Milan, December 1961

This catalogue of Bernard Berenson's collection of paintings does not include those dispersed or destroyed during the war, 1940-45, or those which he presented, at various times, to museums or private individuals, (with the exception of the *Madonna* by Ambrogio Lorenzetti now at the Uffizi). Also excluded are some few works which, although still in the villa, are in a very poor state of conservation or have been repainted too much. The omission of this group is according to Mr. Berenson's own express desire or that of the directors of the " I Tatti " Foundation.

All the paintings are reproduced in colour except six works whose state of conservation is particularly poor. The works are catalogued according to Berenson's attributions. Each listing contains critical comments by the compiler of this catalogue as well as the opinions of other scholars.

Measurements are indicated in centimeters, first height, then width.

Bibliographical references are given in detail at the bottom of each listing. Only the following abbreviations have been used:

B. Berenson 1932 for *Italian Pictures of the Renaissance*, Oxford 1932
B. Berenson 1936 for *Pitture Italiane del Rinascimento*, Milan 1936
B. Berenson 1952 for *The Italian Painters of the Renaissance*, London 1952
B. Berenson 1957 for *Italian Pictures of the Renaissance - Venetian School*, London 1957
A. Venturi for *Storia dell'Arte Italiana*, Milan 1904-1940
R. Van Marle for *The Development of the Italian Schools of Painting*, The Hague 1928-1938

The illustrations in this volume, reproduced from the original masterpieces formerly owned by the late Mr. Bernard Berenson, have been executed with the kind permission of the President and Fellows of Harvard College, present owners of the Berenson Collection at Villa " I Tatti ", Florence.

PLATES

GIOTTO

Colle di Vespignano in Mugello, 1267 (?) – Florence, 1337

Franciscan Saint

Panel, 54 × 39 cm.

CONDITION: good. PROVENANCE: unknown. EXHIBITIONS: Giottesque show, Florence, 1937, No. 101.

" He aims at types which both in face and figure are simple, large-boned, and massive—types, that is to say, which in actual life would furnish the most powerful stimulus to the tactile imagination. Obliged to get the utmost out of his rudimentary light and shade, he makes his scheme of colour of the lightest that his contrasts may be of the strongest. "

B. BERENSON, Italian Painters of the Renaissance - « The Phaidon Press », London, 1952, p. 44.

Berenson considered this painting as a work of Giotto's hand, datable at the time of the Santa Croce frescoes, between 1318 and 1325, and perhaps a fragment of one of the lost polyptychs mentioned by Ghiberti, executed for the Bardi Chapel. Cecchi also accepted this attribution to Giotto and the dating, which was derived from Mather, who assumed that the work dealt with an image of Saint Bonaventura. Toesca, Suida and Gamba accepted the attribution but disagreed regarding the date of the work which they set about 1300, in the period between Assisi and Padua. While Sinibaldi doubts the attribution, Brandi finds in the painting only a " generic linguistic harmony " with Giotto's work; Salvini attributes it to a student who, during Giotto's late period, drew inspiration from the Legend of St. Francis of Assisi. Convincingly, Gnudi assigns this very beautiful work to a very close collaborator of Giotto, perhaps the same who executed some figures of the group at the right in the *Sermon before Onorio* at Assisi, and dates it about 1300.

BIBLIOGRAPHY

F. J. MATHER: *Two Attributions to Giotto*, in « Art Studies », 1925, p. 27 - P. TOESCA: *La Pittura Fiorentina del Trecento*, Florence, 1929, pp. 25, 29 and note 7 - W. SUIDA: *A Panel Painting by Giotto*, « Apollo », 1931, XIII, p. 91 - B. BERENSON: 1932, p. 234 - P. TOESCA: *Giotto*, Enciclopedia Italiana Treccani, 1933, X, II, p. 215 - B. BERENSON: 1936, p. 201 - W. SUIDA: *Giotto - Ausstellung in Florenz*, « Pantheon », 1937, p. 349 - E. CECCHI: *Giotto*, Milan, 1937, p. 103 - C. GAMBA: *Osservazioni sull'Arte di Giotto*, « Rivista d'Arte », 1937, p. 242 - C. BRANDI: *Giotto*, « Le Arti », 1938-39 - P. TOESCA: *Giotto*, Turin, 1941, p. 78 - G. SINIBALDI & G. BRUNETTI: *Pittura Italiana del Duecento e Trecento, Catalogue of the Giotto Exhibition at Florence 1937*, Florence, 1943, p. 327 - SANDBERG-VAVALÀ: *Uffizi Studies*, Florence, 1948, p. 38 - P. TOESCA: *Il Trecento*, Turin, 1951, p. 471 - R. SALVINI: *Tutta la Pittura di Giotto*, Milan, 1952, p. 50 - C. GNUDI: *Giotto*, Milan, 1958, p. 98.

Entombment

Panel, 44.5 × 43 cm. On the back an inscription: " *A picture divided in two : first part representing the Birth of our Saviour, and the second part showing his Entombment: Early Italian School. From the Collection of the late General C. B. Fox.*"

CONDITION: good. PROVENANCE: mentioned for the first time in the sales catalogue of Prince Poniatowski of Florence, in London, 9 February 1839, Lot 103, acquired by Hall. Entered in the General G. B. Fox sale, 4 July 1874, Lot 37, framed together with the *Nativity* now at the Metropolitan Museum of New York, and acquired by Daniell. Subsequently, in the William Fuller Maitland collection, Stanstead House, Essex. Berenson acquired it from Mr. Steinwyer. EXHIBITIONS: Giottesque show, Florence, 1937, No. 106.

" There remains to speak of three small panels, *The Presentation in the Temple* of Mrs. Gardner, the *Crucifixion* and the *Last Supper* at Munich. All these are rather late works, the Crucifixion only in part by Giotto. After serious reflection, I have come to the conclusion that the *Crucifixion* is not even partly by Giotto but, in all probability, by one of his assistants to whom I have assigned the letter C; the *Last Supper* also is not all his: the small panel of Mrs. Gardner comes closer in its dating, to the frescoes of the Peruzzi chapel, showing stylistic similarities to some of these. "

B. BERENSON, Open letter to « Rassegna d'Arte », 1908, p. 45.

As Sirén realizes (1917), the painting should be connected with the series of the stories of Christ to which also belong the *Last Supper*, the *Crucifixion* and the *Christ in Limbo* of the Munich Gallery, as well as the *Adoration of the Magi* of the Metropolitan Museum of New York, and the *Presentation in the Temple* of the Gardner Museum of Boston. Subsequently, the *Pentacost* of the National Gallery of London was deemed as belonging to the same group (cf. M. Davies 1951). Berenson considered this as well as the other panels of the same series, a work of high quality by a close follower of Giotto, executed about the same time as the Peruzzi chapel. Like the other small pictures of the group, this work is generally assigned by scholars to Giotto and his assistants, or to the workshop, or to a follower of Giotto (cf., for various opinions, bibliography on the Giottesque exhibition, catalogue by Sinibaldi-Brunetti, 1943). Hendy, Longhi, L. Venturi, Konody and Zeri decisively attribute this panel to Giotto and place it in varying degrees of relationship with the Padua frescoes, the Peruzzi chapel and the Rimini Crucifix. Longhi considers the seven small pictures and the panels of the Horne, Washington and Châalis polyptych as connected with the Santa Croce frescoes and perhaps belonging to the four paintings mentioned by Ghiberti in Santa Croce. Even if, as Sirén maintains, the history of these works is not definitely established, certainly they were executed on the basis of drawings and under the direct supervision of Giotto, and among these works the Berenson *Entombment* is one of the most beautiful.

BIBLIOGRAPHY

B. BURROUGHS: *The Adoration of the Kings by a Pupil of Giotto*, in « Bulletin of Metropolitan Museum of Art », 1911, VI, p. 216 - O. SIRÈN: *Giotto, and Some of his Followers*, Cambridge, 1917, I, pp. 81, 265. - I. B. SUPINO: *Giotto*, Florence, 1920, p. 271 - W. HAUSENSTEIN: *Giotto*, Berlin, 1923, pp. 15, 191 - F. J. MATHER: *A History of Italian Painting*, New York, 1923, p. 475 - G. WIZTHUM, W. F. VOLBACH: *Die Malerei und Plastik des Mittelalters in Italien*, Wildpark-Potsdam, 1924, p. 265 - R. VAN MARLE: *The Development of the Italian School of Painting*, The Hague, III, 1924, p. 186 - F. J. MATHER: *Two Attributions to Giotto*, in « Art Studies », 1925, p. 31 - C. H. WEIGELT: *Giotto*, Stuttgart, 1925, p. 242 - B. BURROUGHS: *Catalogue of Paintings - The Metropolitan Museum of Art*, New York, 1926, p. 126 - W. F. VOLBACH, H. THODE: *Giotto*, 1926, p. 159, n. 64 - P. HENDY: *The Supposed Painter of Saint Stephen*, in « The Burlington Magazine », 1928, LIII, p. 17 - P. TOESCA: *La Pittura Fiorentina del Trecento*, Florence, 1929, p. 62. - R. FRY *Notes on the Italian Exhibition at Burlington House*, in « The Burlington Magazine », 1930, LVI, p. 83 - R. LONGHI: *Progressi nella Reintegrazione di un Polittico di Giotto*. in « Dedalo » ,1930, XI, p. 290 - P. HENDY: *Gardner Museum Catalogue*, Boston, 1931, p. 171 - L. VENTURI: *Italian Paintings in America*, Milan 1931, pl. XXIV - B. BERENSON: 1932, p. 235 - P. G. KONODY: *Works of Art in the Collection of Viscount Rothermere*, London 1932, pl. III - R. OFFNER: *La Scuola Giottesca*, conference held at Padua in 1937 - E. CECCHI: *Giotto*, 1937, p. 124, Milan - B. BERENSON: 1936, p. 202 - M. SALMI: *La Mostra Giottesca*, in « Emporium », 1937, p. 358. - W. SUIDA: *Giotto-Ausstellung in Florenz*, in « The Pántheon Press », 1937, p. 350 - C. GAMBA: *Osservazioni sull'Arte di Giotto*, in « Rivista d'Arte », 1937, p. 274 - L. COLETTI: *La Mostra Giottesca*, in « Bollettino d'Arte », August 1937, p. 57 - C. BRANDI: *Giotto*, in « Le Arti », 1938-39, pp. 125 (note 24), 126 - L. COLETTI: *I Primitivi - Dall'Arte Benedettina a Giotto*, vol. I; Novara, 1941, p. LIV - T. BORENIUS: *The New Giotto Panel*, « The Burlington Magazine », 1942 p. 217 - G. SINIBALDI, G. BRUNETTI: *Pittura Italiana del Duecento e Trecento, Catalogue of the Giotto Exhibition at Florence*, 1937, Florence, 1943, p. 345, n. 196 - R. LONGHI: *Giudizio sul Duecento*, in « Proporzioni », II, 1948, p. 51 - P. TOESCA: *Il Trecento*, Turin, 1951, pp. 609, 610 - M. DAVIES: *National Gallery Catalogues - The Earlier Italian Schools*, London, 1951, p. 180 - R. SALVINI: *Tutta la Pittura di Giotto*, Milan, 1952, p. 50 - R. OERTEL: *Die Frühzeit der Italienischen Malerei*, Zurich-Vienna, 1953, p. 223, note 167 - F. ZERI: *Due Appunti in Giotto*, in « Paragone », January 1957, p. 78, note 85 - G. GNUDI: *Giotto*, Milan, 1958, pp. 222, 248 (note) - E. CECCHI: *Giotto*, Milan, 1959, p. 31.

GIOTTESQUE MASTER

Crucifixion

Panel, 19.5 × 16 cm.

CONDITION: good. PROVENANCE: unknown. Acquired abroad in 1910. EXHIBITIONS: Giottesque show, Florence, 1937, No. 113.

" When I first saw M. Stoclet's *Nativity* I recognized that I knew a picture by the same hand. It is a *Crucifixion* in my own collection and I wish to believe that it is not merely prejudice in favour of one's own belongings that makes me think that it is intrinsically more worthy of Giotto than the *Nativity*. The modelling of the torso, the heads of the women, the restraint in the expression of grief, the surprised curiosity of the soldiers are all worthy of an artist. Nevertheless, I fail to discover in it an unmistakable parcel of that artistic personality to which we give the name of Giotto. It surely is by another if kindred hand and the purpose of bringing it into the discussion is to enlarge the repertory, as it were, of this unnamed author's types and forms... If I may venture an opinion, he was a painter who was acquainted with the works of all the artists who painted in the nave of the upper church of St. Francis of Assisi. "

B. BERENSON, *Homeless Pictures - The Fourteenth Century Florentines* (from the author's original manuscript, July 1930, pp. 9-11).

Berenson, as may be noted above, tended to assign this work to Giotto; and this attribution was sustained and in part corrected by Fry, and later, Constable and Foster Edward.

Offner added a *Lament for the Dead Christ*, formerly in the Grassi collection, and a *Madonna and Child* of the Vatican Pinacoteca, to the two Stoclet and Berenson panels; attributing the group to an archaicizing master close to Pacino da Buonaguida, belonging to the Giottesque current of the Master of St. Cecilia. Offner's opinion is accepted by Salvini.

Adding an *Annunciation* from a private collection to the series, Longhi said that it dealt with part of a pentatych which he would place among the most sublime works of Stefano Fiorentino.

BIBLIOGRAPHY

R. FRY: *Notes on the Italian Exhibition at Burlington House*, in « The Burlington Magazine », 1930, LVI, p. 78 - *A Commemorative Catalogue of the Exhibition of Italian Art...*, London, 1930, London, 1931, p. 6 - W. G. CONSTABLE: *Quelques Aperçus Suggérés par l'Exposition Italienne de Londres*, in «Gazette des Beaux Arts», 1930, LXXII, p. 277 - E. FOSTER EDWARDS: *Primitives at Burlington House*, in «Art in America», 1930, p. 236 - B. BERENSON: *Quadri senza Casa - Il Trecento Fiorentino*, in « Dedalo », 1930-31, XI, pp. 957 ff. - B. BERENSON: 1932, p. 236 - B. BERENSON: 1936, p. 203 - E. CECCHI: *Giotto*, Milan, 1937, p. 124 - R. OFFNER: *La Scuola Giottesca*, conference held at Padua, 1937 - G. SINIBALDI, G. BRUNETTI: *Pittura Italiana del Duecento e Trecento - Catalogue : Mostra Giottesca di Firenze nel 1937*, Florence, 1943, p. 369 - R. LONGHI: *Giudizio sul Duecento*, in « Proporzioni », II, 1948, p. 52 - R. LONGHI: *Stefano Fiorentino*, in « Paragone » n. 13, January 1951, p. 25 - P. TOESCA: *Il Trecento*, Turin, 1951, p. 610 n. 133 - R. SALVINI: *Tutta la Pittura di Giotto*, Milan, 1952, p. 51 - E. CECCHI: *Giotto*, Milan, 1959, p. 32.

BERNARDO DADDI

Florence, active 1312-1345

Madonna and Child with two Angels

Panel, 83 × 54 cm.

CONDITION: good. PROVENANCE: William Beattie collection, Stirlingshire, Scotland. Then in the Sully collection, London. Berenson acquired the work in 1911.

" Daddi was the earliest of the Florentine painters deliberately to throw himself into the Gothic movement. He was, however, kept back by the severe discipline he received under Giotto and did not run to the excesses of other followers of Giovanni Pisano, but compromised upon an easy clarity, a noble, gracious and refined spacing reminding us more of what sculptors had done in Northern France under St. Louis than of the calligraphic rhythms already prevailing among his own Parisian and Picard contemporaries."

B. BERENSON, *Homeless Pictures - The Fourteenth Century Florentines* (from the author's original manuscript, July 1930, pp. 14-15).

Formerly attributed to Taddeo Gaddi, as an old label on the back of the panel indicates, this celebrated painting is unanimously considered one of Daddi's masterpieces. Longhi discerned in it a manner derived from the sweetly solemn, poetic style of a privately-owned Maso *Madonna* which he had attributed to Puccio di Simone. The Berenson picture, which Offner feels was perhaps inspired by the Lorenzettis, may be dated about 1340.

BIBLIOGRAPHY

F. MASON PERKINS: *Note su Alcuni Quadri del Museo Cristiano nel Vaticano* in « Rassegna d'Arte », 1906, VI, p. 107 n. 1 - A. VENTURI: 1907, vol. V, p. 521, note - B. KHVOSHINSKY - M. SALMI: *I Pittori Toscani dal XIII al XVI Secolo*, Rome, 1914, vol. 2, p. 23 - O. SIRÉN: *Giotto and Some of his Followers*, Cambridge, 1917, pp. 175, 176, 270 - R. OFFNER: *Italian Pictures at the New York Historical Society and Elsewhere ;* part one - R. OFFNER: *Italian Pictures at the New York Historical Society and Elsewhere* in « Art in America »; 1919, VII, pp. 149, 151 - R. VAN MARLE: 1924, III, pp. 384, 388 - G. VITZTHUM, W. F. VOLBACH: *Die Malerei und Plastik des Mittelalters in Italien*, Wildpark-Potsdam, 1924, p. 298 - R. OFFNER: *Studies in Florentine Paintings*, New York, 1927, p. 108, n. 24 - R. OFFNER: *Corpus of Florentine Painting*, New York, 1930, Sect. III, vol. III; p. 52, plate XIII - B. BERENSON: 1932, p. 166 - B. BERENSON: 1936, p. 143 - L. COLETTI: *I Primitivi, II*, Novara, 1946, p. XLVIII - R. LONGHI: *Qualità e Industria in Taddeo Gaddi ed Altri*, in « Paragone », n. 111, 1958, p. 10 - G. PACCAGNINI: *Bernardo Daddi* in « Enciclopedia Universale dell'Arte », Venice-Rome, 1958, IV, pp. 182 ff.

IV

BERNARDO DADDI

Crucifixion - on the back: *St. Christopher*

Tabernacle 40 × 15 cm.

CONDITION: good. PROVENANCE: B. Berenson acquired this tabernacle on the Florentine market, 1895.

" He had great technical ability, worked easily, and must have been prolific. He turned out many of those portable triptychs which served for household chapels, or were carried about on journeys. They doubtless were sold abroad and not least at the Fairs of Champagne. They and their like by other Florentine painters were perhaps more efficient carriers of Tuscan art to Paris, to Picardy, to Flanders than the stationary frescoes at Avignon."

B. BERENSON, *Homeless Pictures - The Fourteenth Century Florentines* (from the author's original manuscript, July 1930. p. 15).

B. Berenson attributed this tabernacle to Daddi. Offner considers it a work of a very close collaborator. The quality would seem to be worthy of the Master himself.

BIBLIOGRAPHY

W. SUIDA: *Studien zur Trecentomalerei*, I, in « Repertorium für Kunstwissenschaft », 1904, p. 388 - W. SUIDA: *Studien zur Trecentomalerei*, III, in « Repertorium für Kunstwissenschaft », 1906, pp. 110-11 - A. VENTURI: 1907, vol. V, p. 520, n. 2 - B. KHVOSHINSKY - M. SALMI: *I Pittori Toscani dal XIII al XVI Secolo*, II - *I Fiorentini del Trecento*, Rome, 1914, p. 23 - O. SIRÉN: *Giotto and Some of his Followers*, Cambridge, 1917, I, p. 270 - W. SUIDA: *Meisterwerke Italienischer Malerei*, I, in « Belvedere », 1923, p. 25 - E. SANDBERG-VAVALÀ: *Opere Inedite di B. D.* in « Cronache d'Arte », 1927, pp. 382, 387, note - B. BERENSON: 1932, p. 166 - R. OFFNER: *Corpus of Florentine Painting*, New York, 1934, Sect. III, vol. IV, p. 68, pl. XXX, XXXI - B. BERENSON: 1936, p. 143 - K. STEINWEG: *Ein Verschollens Tabernakel von B. D.*, in « Mitteilungen des Kunsthistorischen Institutes in Florenz », 1953, VII, pl. I, p. 68.

FOLLOWER OF BERNARDO DADDI

Florence, XIVth Century

St. Catherine

Panel, 81 × 36 cm.

CONDITION: greatly deteriorated with considerable flaking of pigment. Repainted and restored. PROVENANCE: acquired in Florence.

Attributed by B. Berenson to the school of Bernardo Daddi, Offner subsumes this polyptych panel in the group by the Master whom he named " Master of the Domenican Images " on the basis of the small panel in the sacristy of Santa Maria Novella, Florence. As is known, this personality, formerly pointed out by Sirén (1926) who provided him with a *corpus* built around the polyptych of the Lord Lee Collection in Richmond, was named by Berenson "The Master of Terenzano" (cf. in " Dedalo ", 1931, XI, pp. 981, ff.). However, Berenson did not include his own *Saint Catherine* in the catalogue of this anonymous follower of Daddi. According to Offner, the panel was part of the same polyptych to which the *Saint Margaret* of the L. Bellini collection, Florence, belongs.

BIBLIOGRAPHY

R. OFFNER: *Corpus of Florentine Painting*, New York, 1930, Sect. III, vol. II, Part II, Addenda, plate XII.

NARDO DI CIONE

Florence, documented from 1343 to 1365

St. Benedict receives a young monk

Panel, 16 × 33 cm.

CONDITION: this small panel has been trimmed a bit on the bottom and on the left side. The painting is well preserved. PROVENANCE: unknown.

As Steinweg realized in 1938, this is the predella of the painting of *St. Benedict* (No. 2259), in the National Museum, Stockholm. Offner considers it among the Master's earliest works. In this little panel, Nardo di Cione reaches one of the peaks of his serene, austere art.

BIBLIOGRAPHY

O. SIRÉN: in « Kult och Kunst », Stockholm, 1907, p. 134 n., p. 141 - O. SIRÉN: *Giottino*, Lipsia, 1908, p. 89 - O. SIRÉN: *Addenda und Errata zu meinem Giottino-Buch*, in « Monatshefte für Kunstwissenschaft », 1908, I, p. 1122 - B. BERENSON: *The Florentine Painters of the Renaissance*, New York-London, 1909, p. 161 - B. KHVOSHINSKY, M. SALMI: *I Pittori Toscani dal XIII al XVI Secolo*, Rome, 1914, II, p. 30. - O. SIRÉN: *Giotto and Some of his Followers*, Cambridge, 1917, I, p. 276 - R. VAN MARLE: 1924, III, p. 488 - R. OFFNER: *Nardo di Cione and his Triptych in the Goldman Collection*, in « Art in America », 1924, XII, pp. 101, 111. - G. VITZTHUM, W. F. VOLBACH: *Die Malerei und Plastik des Mittelalters in Italien*, Wildpark-Potsdam, 1924, p. 304 - R. OFFNER: *Studies in Florentine Painting*, New York, 1927, pp. 100, 106 - B. BERENSON: 1932, p. 383 - B. BERENSON: 1936, p. 329 - H. D. GRONAU: *Andrea Orcagna und Nardo di Cione*, Berlin, 1937, p. 85 n. 140 - K. STEINWEG: *Review of Gronau*, in « The Burlington Magazine » 1938, LXXII, p. 96 - R. OFFNER: *Corpus of Florentine Painting*, New York, 1960, Sect. IV, vol. II, pp. 11, 12.

NARDO DI CIONE

St. Anthony Abbott

Panel, 74 × 32 cm.

CONDITION: fragmentary panel, originally ogival. Much flaking of pigment. The Saint may once have been full-figure: certainly the panel has been cut on all sides, perhaps, as Offner supposes, to remove the worm-eaten parts. PROVENANCE: acquired in Florence around 1927.

Berenson attributed this fragment of the right panel of a polyptych to Nardo di Cione. According to Offner, however, it is the work of a mediocre painter who fell under Nardo's influence after having shaped his style among various other schools of painting.

BIBLIOGRAPHY

B. BERENSON: 1932, p. 383 - B. BERENSON: 1936, p. 329 - R. OFFNER: *Corpus of Florentine Painting*, New York, 1960, Sect. IV, vol. II, pp. 79, 80.

GIOVANNI DA MILANO

Born, Caversaccio di Como. Active in Lombardy and Florence from 1345 to after 1369

Gabriel and *the Virgin*

Two Panels, 17×13 cm. each.

CONDITION: good. PROVENANCE: gift of Don Guido Cagnola.

" Although a foreigner by birth and training, Giovanni da Milano, during his long sojourn in Florence, came under the influence of the Orcagnas, imbided something of their idiom and a good deal of their fervour, and himself, in turn, exerted an influence over such an artist as Andrea da Firenze. As there are pictures of both of them among our lost sheep, this is the place to speak of them.

Giovanni was one of the great men of the Trecento, and I wish I knew how he got by his style. He was ever so much more plastic than any of his Italian contemporaries. Not only are the relations of his voids to his solids in the nature of full or half relief, but his planes are differentiated and approached in a way that anticipates the Quattrocento. At times he depicts a sort of glorified actuality, as did the more refined painters of the High Renaissance. And his tone, curiously enough, is almost as silvery as in certain Milanese painters like Foppa and Bergognone, of so much later a period. Altogether a mysterious figure."

B. BERENSON, *Homeless Pictures - The Fourteenth Century Florentines*, (from the author's original manuscript p. 53).

L. Venturi attributed these small panels to Giovanni da Milano, because of a label on the back of one of the panels. Berenson, Marabottini and Toesca, also assigned these works to the same artist, describing them as among the most Siena-like works of the artist. However, these fragments of the wings of a small triptych possess certain stylistic characteristics which do not permit an unqualified acceptance of the proposed attribution. Products of an ambience very close to Giovanni da Milano, they are probably the work of a Florentine Master very much influenced by " Giottino ", perhaps of the " Puccio di Simone " group (Longhi).

BIBLIOGRAPHY

B. BERENSON: 1936, p. 210. - A. MARABOTTINI: *Giovanni da Milano*, Florence, 1950, p. 88 - P. TOESCA: *Il Trecento*, Turin, 1951, p. 762, n. 293.

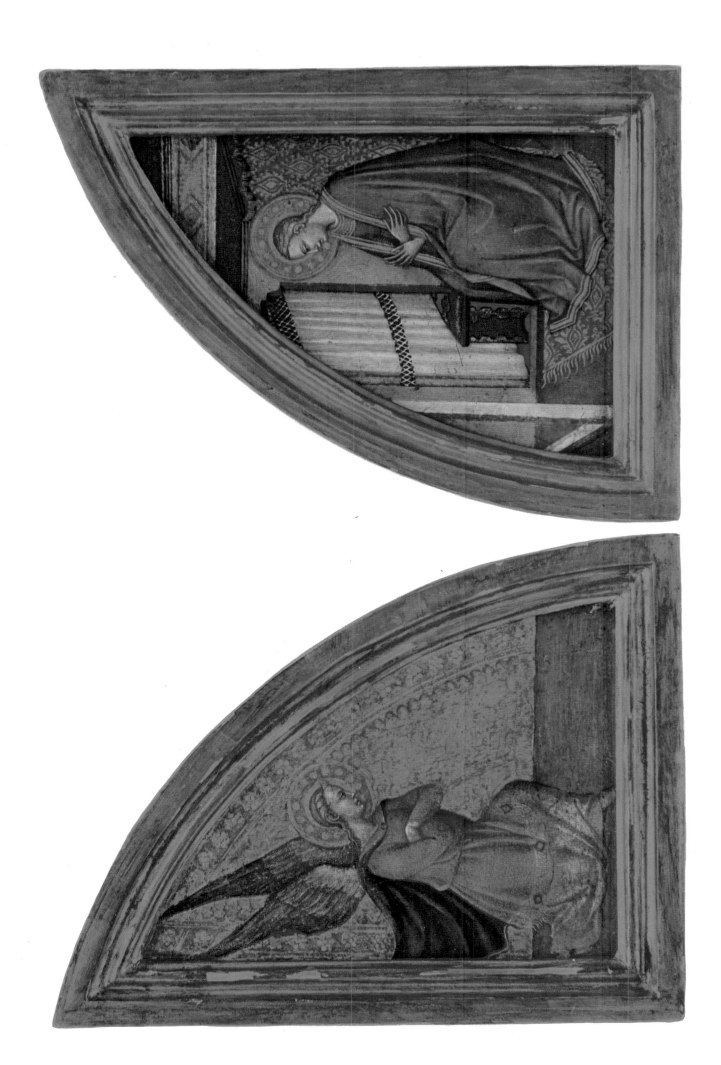

IX

JACOPO DI CIONE

Florence, active 1365-1398

Madonna enthroned between Saints and Angels

Panel: 64 × 38 cm.

CONDITION: good. PROVENANCE: acquired by Berenson from Dowdeswell and Dowdeswell, London 1911. Formerly in the Toscanelli Collection, and then in the Charles Butter collection.

" Jacopo di Cione is one of the most baffling problems in Florentine art. I suspect that, like his brothers, he started out with the ideas and stage properties, so to speak, of Maso, in that master's Gothic, Lorenzetti phase. He then seems to have painted with and for Andrea, and I am inclined to believe that he executed, if he did not entirely design, most of the pictures that we suppose to have come out of Andrea's workshop. It would further seem that he was so impressed by the types and proportions and attitudes that Andrea was carving on the famous tabernacle which still clutters up Orsanmichele that his own later and independent manner was influenced by them. After the death of his more famous brothers he lived on some thirty years till toward the end of the century, he remaining the chief carrier of the Maso-Orcagna traditions."

B. BERENSON, - *Homeless Pictures - The Fourteenth Century Florentines* (From the author's original manuscript, July 1930, p. 33).

While in the Toscanelli Collection, the work was attributed to the School of Orcagna. It was shown at the Royal Academy, London, in 1884 as a Venetian primitive; and at the New Gallery, London, in 1893-94 as a painting by Bernardo Daddi. Offner accepts Berenson's suggested attribution of this altar to Jacopo. Derivation from Daddi, although fossilized by the school of Orcagna, is evident in this work, datable about the seventh decade of the century.

BIBLIOGRAPHY

R. OFFNER: *The Mostra del Tesoro di Firenze Sacra, I*, in « The Burlington Magazine », 1933, LXIII, I, p. 84 n. 59 - R. OFFNER: *Corpus of Florentine Painting*, New York, 1947, Sect. III, vol. V, p. 153 - B. BERENSON: 1932, p. 274 - B. BERENSON: 1936, p. 235.

X

SEGNA DI BONAVENTURA

Siena, active between 1298-1326

St. Thomas

Panel, 63 × 37 cm. Inscribed on the gold ground—ST. THOMAS.

CONDITION: good; the colours have lost some of their tone. PROVENANCE: unknown.

" Duccio, however, not only trained his followers to conceptions and methods necessarily his own, but by furnishing to an emotional people like the Sienese an art that
appealed to the feelings, he compelled the painters who came after him to deal in that
perniciously popular article, expressive Illustration."

B. BERENSON, *Italian Painters of the Renaissance* - « The Phaidon Press », London, p. 98.

Perkins attributed this polyptych panel to the School of Duccio; Van Marle to one of the followers of
Segna who, in his judgment, created the *Platt Madonna* and the *Magdalen* of the Museum of Fine Arts,
Boston. Berenson assigned this work to Segna himself, inasmuch as it presents many stylistic character-
istics common to the " Bartolommeo Bulgarini " group which Meiss re-integrated.

BIBLIOGRAPHY

F. MASON PERKINS: *Appunti sulla Mostra Ducciana a Siena*, II, in « Rassegna d'Arte », 1913, pp. 38-39 - R. VAN MARLE: vol. II, 1923, p. 143 - B. BEREN-
SON: 1932, p. 523 - B. BERENSON: 1936, p. 450.

XI

SIMONE MARTINI

Siena, 1284 - Avignon, 1344

St. Lucy and *St. Catherine*

Two panels of a polyptych, 51 × 40 cm. and 54 × 41 cm. A later inscription on the frame of the *St. Lucy* indicates it as a *Magdalen*.

CONDITION: considerable loss of tone. Restored in large part. PROVENANCE: unknown.

" To convey his feeling for beauty and grace and splendour, Simone possessed means more than sufficient. He was master of colour, as few have been before him or after him. He had a feeling for line always remarkable and once, at least, attaining to a degree of perfection not to be surpassed. He understood decorative effects as a great musician understands his instruments."

B. BERENSON, *Italian Painters of the Renaissance* - « The Phaidon Press », London, pp. 99-100.

Berenson, Perkins, Van Marle and De Rinaldis attributed these *Little Saints* to Simone. However, Weigelt considered them workshop productions. Concurring with Weigelt, Laclotte relates them to the *Saint Catherine* of Mans. Paccagnini and Volpe join them with the "Master of the Palazzo Venezia" group. Datable toward 1320, these paintings certainly possess the tender grace characteristic of the "Master of the Palazzo Venezia", but considering their state of preservation, a definite judgment would be imprudent.

BIBLIOGRAPHY

B. BERENSON: *The Central Italian Painters of the Renaissance*, New York-London, 1909, p. 252 - F. MASON PERKINS: *Ancora dei Dipinti Sconosciuti della Scuola Senese* in « Rassegna d'Arte Senese », 1908, pp. 7, 8 - J. A. CROWE, G. B. CAVALCASELLE: *A History of Painting in Italy*, (L. Douglas ed.), London, 1908, III, p. 70 n. - J. A. CROWE, G. B. CAVALCASELLE: *A New History of Painting in Italy*, (E. Hutton ed.), London, 1909, I, p. 57, n. - R. VAN MARLE: *Simone Martini et les Peintres de son École*, Strassbourg, 1920 - R. VAN MARLE *The Development of the Italian School of Painting*, The Hague, 1923, p. 173 - K. WEIGELT: *La Pittura Senese del Trecento*, Bologna, 1930, p. 72 n. 44 - G. EDGELL: *A History of Sienese Painting*, New York, 1932, p. 80 n. 18 - F. MASON PERKINS: *Simone Martini* in « Thieme-Becker », XXXI, 1937, p. 67 - A. DE RINALDIS: *Simone Martini*, Rome, 1936, p. 64 - B. BERENSON: 1932, p. 534 - B. BERENSON: 1936, p. 459 - G. KAFTAL: *Iconography of the Saints in Tuscan Painting*, Florence, 1952, p. 644 - G. PACCAGNINI: *Simone Martini*, Milan, 1955, p. 98 - M. LACLOTTE: *De Giotto à Bellini - Catalogue de l'Exposition*, Paris, 1956, p. 29 - C. VOLPE: *Precisazioni sul Barna e sul Maestro di Palazzo Venezia*, in « Arte Antica e Moderna », 1960, issue 10, p. 153.

LIPPO MEMMI

Siena, documented from 1317 - died 1356

Madonna enthroned between Saints Michael and Gabriel. Saints and curtain-bearing Angels. In the frame, two tondi with *Busts of Prophets.*

Panel, 179 × 109 cm.

CONDITION: the colours have lost tone somewhat. PROVENANCE: acquired by B. Berenson in Paris, after 1909.

Van Marle and Weigelt, and subsequently Berenson, attributed this work to Lippo Memmi. Then it was integrated with the " Master of the Palazzo Venezia " group. Although maintaining the Lippo attribution, Cecchi and Edgell also noted that the work was similar in many ways to the Palazzo Venezia *Madonna* with which Mason Perkins had connected it. In addition, Van Marle put forward the name of Donato. This *Madonna* was the central panel of a polyptych, two wings of which are known, with figures of *Saints Ansano* (or *Victor* or *Galgano?*) and *Catherine* (*?*) at the Copenhagen Museum where they are catalogued as Lippo Memmi. The paintings may be dated about 1340.

BIBLIOGRAPHY

J. A. CROWE, G. B. CAVALCASELLE: *A New History of Painting in Italy*, (E. Hutton ed.) London, 1909, I, p. 57 n. - R. VAN MARLE: *Simone Martini et les Peintres de son École*, Strassbourg, 1920 - M. SALMI: *Simone Martini e i Pittori della sua Scuola*, in « Rassegna d'Arte Senese », 1922, p. 14 - R. VAN MARLE: *The Development of the Italian School of Painting*, The Hague, II, 1923, p. 254, V, 1925, p. 18, n. 1 - K. WEIGELT: *Lippo Memmi* in « Thieme-Becker », XXIII, 1929 - K. WEIGELT: *La Pittura Senese del Trecento*, Bologna, 1930, p. 73, note 44, p. 78, note 63 - K. WEIGELT: *Minor Simonesque Masters*, in « Apollo », XIX, July 1931, p. 6 - G. EDGELL: *A History of Sienese Painting*, New York, 1932, p. 83 n. 20, p. 103 n. 161 - F. MASON PERKINS: *Pitture Senesi*, Siena, 1933, p. 132 (originally printed in « La Diana », 1932, p. 52) - B. BERENSON: 1932, p. 359 - C. BRANDI: *La R. Pinacoteca di Siena*, Rome, 1933, p. 173 - B. BERENSON: 1936, p. 309 - E. SANDBERG-VAVALÀ: *Some Partial Reconstruction I*, in « The Burlington Magazine », 1937, p. 177 - E. CECCHI: *Trecentisti Senesi*, Milan, 1948, pp. 92, 183 - H. VOLLMER: *Meister der Madonna in Palazzo Venezia* in « Allgemeines Lexikon », LXXXVII, 1950, p. 208 - *Catalogue of Old Foreign Paintings*, Royal Museum of Fine Arts, Copenhagen, 1951, pp. 193, 194 - E. CARLI: *La Pittura Senese*, Milan, 1955, p. 150 - C. VOLPE: *Precisazioni sul Barna e sul Maestro di Palazzo Venezia* in « Arte Antica e Moderna », 1960, issue 10; pp. 154 ff.

PIETRO LORENZETTI

Siena, documented from about 1306 to 1348

RELIQUARY: *Madonna and Child with kneeling Donor.*

Panel, with frame 61 × 33 cm. Painted part alone, 33 × 14 cm.

CONDITION: panel cradled; the colours are slightly cracking and flaking. PROVENANCE: unknown.

" Singularly gifted, [the Lorenzetti brothers] . . . display their gifts but listlessly. Beauty, which they felt with passion, form, which Giovanni Pisano and Giotto had so amply revealed to them, even the sense of human significance with which they were aglow, they sooner or later sacrificed, either to the mere representation of things, or to the vain endeavour to body forth dim, infinite meanings."

B. BERENSON, Italian Painters of the Renaissance – « The Phaidon Press », London, p. 100.

This is the front of a two-sided painted reliquary panel. The back, depicting *Christ enthroned, blessing, and a Franciscan friar with a parchment scroll*, was removed and is now in a private collection at Rome. This part of the reliquary was found and recognized by F. Zeri.
Berenson dated this very beautiful reliquary somewhat after 1325 and attributed it to Lorenzetti. Perkins, Van Marle, Cecchi, Ragghianti, Zeri, Gregori, and Laclotte also considered it as the work of the Master. On the other hand, Dewald, Weigelt, Sinibaldi, Peter, Coletti and Meiss connect it with the group which they call the " Dijon Master ", a group which might very well be fitted into the range of Pietro's activity. Zeri's proposed dating is between 1330—1340, that is, similar to the dates which Cecchi had formerly put forward (1330—1335).

BIBLIOGRAPHY

L. GIELLY: *Pietro Lorenzetti* in «Revue de l'Art Ancien et Moderne», XXXII, 1912, note p. 454 - F. MASON PERKINS: *Vita di Pietro Laurati...*, Florence, 1912, p. 37 - B. BERENSON: *Essays in the Story of Sienese Painting*, New York, 1918, p. 19 - R. VAN MARLE: vol. II, 1923, p. 337 - E. T. DEWALD: *Pietro Lorenzetti* in «Art Studies», 1929, pp. 154 ff. - H. C. WEIGELT: *La Pittura Senese del Trecento*, Bologna, 1930, p. 80 note 70 - E. CECCHI: *Piero Lorenzetti*, Milan, 1930, pp. 88, 138 - B. BERENSON: 1932, p. 393 - A. PETER: *Contributi alla Conoscenza di Pietro Lorenzetti e della sua Scuola*, in «La Diana» 1933, p. 184 - G. SINIBALDI: *I Lorenzetti*, Florence, 1933, p. 181 - B. BERENSON: 1936, p. 251 - L. COLETTI: *I Primitivi*, II, Novara, 1948, p. XXIV - E. CECCHI: *Trecentisti Senesi*, Milan, 1948, p. 109 - C. L. RAGGHIANTI: *Collezioni americane, La collezione Rabinowitz*, in «La Critica d'Arte», XXVII, 1949, p. 78 - M. MEISS: *Painting in Florence and in Siena after the Black Death*, Princeton, 1951, p. 42 n. 119 - F. ZERI: *Reconstruction of a two-sided Reliquary Panel by Pietro Lorenzetti*, in «The Burlington Magazine», 1953, p. 245 - M. GREGORI: *Due Opere di Pietro Lorenzetti* in «Paragone», 1953, p. 79 - M. LACLOTTE: *De Giotto à Bellini - Catalogue de l'Exposition*, Paris, 1956, p. 11.

AMBROGIO LORENZETTI

Siena, mentioned from 1319 to 1348

Madonna and Child

Panel, 106 × 52 cm.

CONDITION: good. PROVENANCE: acquired in Florence from Dr. Paoletti. The painting was given by Mr. Berenson to the Uffizi Gallery in the summer of 1959.

This very lovely *Madonna* was perhaps already known to de Nicola who, in 1922, mentions a *Virgin with Child* of a private collection that should be related, (as the central panel) to two Saints, Nicholas and Proculus, of the Bandini Museum of Fiesole. The work was mentioned in print for the first time by Rowley, who, although he still connected it with the Bandini saints, unjustifiably attributed the marvelous tryptych to a minor figure whom he invented and called " the Rofeno Master " The three stupendous panels, among Ambrogio's masterpieces, now at the Uffizi, should be considered in connection with the information that might be obtained from old historical and critical literary works concerning the polyptychs in the church of St. Proculus in Florence. A good analysis and discussion of the complex problem has been made by Becherucci who, somewhat modifiying the suggestions put forward by Sandberg-Vavalà, Offner, and Volpe, identifies the *Madonna* with the one dated 1332, seen by Cinelli in the Arrighi Chapel in San Procolo (c.f. G. Cinelli: *Le Bellezze della città di Firenze*, Florence, 1677, p. 389). The 1332 dating would apply perfectly to the Berenson picture: the inscription, perhaps on the frame, must have been lost when the work was removed from its original assemblage.

BIBLIOGRAPHY

F. MASON PERKINS: *Alcune Opere d'Arte Ignorate - Two panels of A. Lorenzetti*, in « Rassegna d'Arte », 1918, n. 7-8, pp. 105 ff. - G. DE NICOLA: *Il Soggiorno Fiorentino di Ambrogio Lorenzetti*, « Bollettino d'Arte », 1922, II, p. 52 - B. BERENSON: 1932, p. 280 - B. BERENSON: 1936, p. 250 - E. SANDBERG-VAVALÀ: *Uffizi Studies*, Florence, 1948, p. 85 - E. SANDBERG-VAVALÀ: *Sienese Studies*, Florence, 1953, p. 139 - R. OFFNER: *Corpus of Florentine Painting*, New York, 1956, Sect. III, vol. VI, p. 158, note 2 - G. ROWLEY: *Ambrogio Lorenzetti*, Princeton, 1958, pp. 47, 70. - C. VOLPE: *Nuove proposte sui Lorenzetti*, in « Arte Antica e Moderna », 1960, issue 11, pp. 271 ff. - L. BECHERUCCI: *Il dono di Bernardo Berenson alla Galleria degli Uffizi*, in « Bollettino d'Arte », 1961, n. 1-11, January-June, pp. 33 ff.

UGOLINO LORENZETTI

Sienese master, active about mid XIVth Century

Crucifixion

Panel, 39.5 × 26.5 cm.

CONDITION: good. PROVENANCE: Berenson wrote (cf. *Essays in the study of Sienese Painting*, 1918) that the merchant who sold him this work said it came from Rugano where a companion piece still remained.

" One is an upright panel in my collection and the other is an oblong panel, probably part of a *predella*, in the Louvre. In the upright one, the treatment remains Ducciesque, with episodes culled, as it were, from the sublime *Crucifixion* in the *Maestas*. Our master betrays himself first in the warmth, brilliance and radiance of the colour, surpassing in this respect, no doubt only because of its better preservation, all his other works, and then in the types, in the astonished expression, in the prominence given to the whites of the eyes, and in a way the draperies have of stretching, for no reason, into angularity or flatness. It is a design he must have executed between the Santa Croce Polyptych and the Fogliano Triptych... Our author was, as we have seen, an artist who started as the pupil of Ugolino and ended as the follower of the Lorenzetti. I propose, therefore, to designate him, until archives one day yield up the secret of how his contemporaries called him, by the linked name of his two teachers, 'Ugolino Lorenzetti.'"

B. BERENSON, *Essays in the study of Sienese Painting*, New York, 1918, pp. 25, 35.

This work is almost unanimously considered to be by the hand of the Master whom Berenson called " Ugolino Lorenzetti ", and whom Dewald named " The Master of the Ovile Madonna ". Meiss suggests that the latter figure might be identified with Bartolommeo Bulgarini (cf. *Rivista d'Arte*, 1936, p. 113 ff.). Carli accepts Meiss' proposal. In 1913, Perkins had assigned it to a Master rather close to Duccio, and Weigelt had related it to " Ugolino Lorenzetti " without directly attributing it to the Master. Peter also considers it a work of a follower. It is, however, undoubtedly among the most typical works of the group.

BIBLIOGRAPHY

F. MASON PERKINS: *Appunti sulla Mostra Ducciana a Siena*, II, in « Rassegna d'Arte », 1913, p. 38 note II - B. BERENSON: *Essays in the Study of Sienese Painting*, New York, 1918, pp. 25 ff. (Reprinted from « Art in America », 1917, pp. 259 ff. - 1918, pp. 25 ff.) - R. VAN MARLE: *Dipinti Senesi nel Museo Arcivescovile di Utrecht* in « Bollettino d'Arte », II, 1922-23, p. 564-65 - R. VAN MARLE: Vol. II, 1923, pp. 115, 121, 125 - E. T. DEWALD: *The Master of the Ovile Madonna* in « Art Studies », I, 1923, pp. 45 ff. - P. HENDY: *Ugolino Lorenzetti: Some further Attributions*, in « The Burlington Magazine », 1929, p. 232 - E. T. DEWALD: *Pietro Lorenzetti* in « Art Studies », 1929, pp. 154 ff. - C. H. WEIGELT: *La Pittura Senese del Trecento*, Bologna, 1930, p. 70, note 34 - A. PETER: *Ugolino Lorenzetti e il Maestro Ovile*, in « Rivista d'Arte », 1931, pp. 42-43 - B. BERENSON: 1932, p. 295 - G. H. EDGELL: *A History of Sienese Painting*, New York, 1932, pp. 116, 147 - B. BERENSON: 1936, p. 253 - M. MEISS: *Ugolino Lorenzetti* in « The Art Bulletin », XIII, 1931, pp. 376 note, p. 379 - E. CECCHI: *Trecentisti Senesi*, Milan, 1948, pp. 61, 176 - L. COLETTI: *I Primitivi*, II, Novara, 1948, p. XXV.

SIENESE MASTER

FIRST HALF OF THE XIVᵗʰ CENTURY, FOLLOWER OF THE BROTHER'S LORENZETTI

POLYPTYCH: *Madonna and Child* with (from left to right) *St. Francis, St. John the Baptist, St. Augustine, the Magdalen.* In the cusps (in the same order): *St. James, St. Paul, the Redeemer, St. Peter and St. Ludwig of Tolosa.*

113 × 57 cm., central panel; the others, 100 × 38.5 cm. each.

CONDITION: good. PROVENANCE: acquired from the Toscanelli collection.

Perkins attributed this work to a Master similar to " Ugolino Lorenzetti " and the " Master of the Ovile Madonna " (that is, the " Bartolommeo Bulgarini " group). The same scholar also connected it with the Triptych of St. Giovanni d'Asso which Berenson attributed to Ugolino of Siena. Brandi finds some points of contact between this work and Triptych No. 54 of the Siena Pinacoteca which he assigns to a follower of Pietro Lorenzetti, someone like the " Dijon Master." There is no question that the work, showing strong influences of Pietro Lorenzetti, should be related to the " Bartolommeo Bulgarini " workshop.

BIBLIOGRAPHY

F. MASON PERKINS: *Pitture Senesi*, Siena, 1933, p. 60 (reprinted from an article published in « La Diana », 1931, p. 27) - C. BRANDI: *La R. Pinacoteca di Siena*, Rome, 1933, p. 158 - B. BERENSON: 1932, p. 529 - B. BERENSON: 1936, p. 455.

BARNA

Sienese master. active during the second half of the XIVth Century

Madonna of Humility

Panel, 39 × 21 cm.

CONDITION: panel cradled; colours reveal an old cleaning. PROVENANCE: unknown.

" Barna, Bartolo di Fredi, and Taddeo di Bartolo at times catch a glow from the splendour of Simone Martini and the Lorenzetti."

B. BERENSON, *Italian Painters of the Renaissance* – « The Phaidon Press », London, p. 103.

Although Berenson attributed this painting to Barna, Perkins assigned it to a Sienese of the last quarter of the XIVth century, bearing vague similarities to Barna's style. Meiss dated it toward 1365, and in view of its similar composition, considers it related to the *Lanz Madonna*, which he attributes to the workshop of Bartolommeo Bulgarini, that is, " Ugolino Lorenzetti ". In fact, there are very strong resemblances with " Ugolino Lorenzetti's " style. I believe that the *Lanz Madonna*, which is of inferior quality, derives from the Berenson panel.

BIBLIOGRAPHY

B. BERENSON: *Italian Paintings - Catalogue of a Collection of Paintings and some Art Objects*, J. G. Johnson, Philadelphia, 1913, p. 54 - F. MASON PERKINS: *Pitture Senesi*, Siena, 1933, p. 61 (originally printed in «La Diana», 1931) - M. MEISS: *Ugolino Lorenzetti* in «The Art Bulletin», 1931, XIII, p. 388, n. 20 - B. BERENSON, 1932, p. 41 - M. MEISS: *The Madonna of Humility* in « The Art Bulletin », XVIII, 1936, p. 437, note - M. MEISS: *Painting in Florence and in Siena after the Black Death*, Princeton, 1951, p. 134, note 7.

PAOLO DI GIOVANNI FEI

Siena, documented from 1369 to 1411

Madonna enthroned with Angel curtain-bearers and Saints Peter, Paul, Andrew, the Baptist, Catherine, James, Anthony Abbott, and another Saint. In the lateral cusps: *Annunciation.* In the pinnacle of the central cusp: *Crucifixion.*

Panel 57.5 × 56 cm.

CONDITION: fair, colour dirty. PROVENANCE: perhaps acquired from G. Brauer, Paris 1910.

" Fei was an incorrect draughtsman, and more often an infelicitous colourist. His types are apt to be heavy, ugly, almost caricatures. All the same, he has remained a favourite ever since attention was drawn to his artistic personality. There is a captivating innocence and good humour about him and he succeeds in communicating something of his *joie de travailler.*"

B. BERENSON, *Homeless Pictures - The Fourteenth Century Sienese* (from the author's original manuscript, July 1930, p. 75).

Typical work of Fei, related to the period of the triptych in the Siena Pinacoteca, No. 183.

BIBLIOGRAPHY

B. BERENSON: 1932, p. 183 - G. EDGELL: *A History of Sienese Painting.* New York, 1932, p. 176 - B. BERENSON; 1936, p. 157.

TADDEO DI BARTOLO

Siena, c. 1362-1422

Christ and the twelve Apostles

Panel: 23 × 134 cm.

CONDITION: damaged during the war, and restored by G. Marchig. PROVENANCE: unknown.

" [Taddeo di Bartolo] was a mediocrity, a sort of Lo Spagna of his period, and few were the Sienese painters then beginning who did not feel his influence."

B. BERENSON, *Homeless Pictures - The Fourteenth Century Sienese* (from the author's original manuscript. July 1930, p. 26).

We do not know the polyptych to which this beautiful predella belonged. Datable a little after 1410, the work reveals Taddeo's highest qualities as a serene and severe " portraitist. "

BIBLIOGRAPHY

F. MASON PERKINS: *Ancora dei Dipinti Sconosciuti della Scuola Senese* in « Rassegna d'Arte Senese », 1908, I, p. 8 - B. BERENSON: *The Central Italian Painters of the Renaissance*, New York-London, 1909, p. 256 - J. A. CROWE, G. B. CAVALCASELLE: *A New History of Painting in Italy*, (E. Hutton ed.), London, 1909, I, p. 113 n. - F. MASON PERKINS: *Taddeo di Bartolo* in « Thieme-Becker », XXXII, 1938, p. 396 - B. BERENSON: 1932, p. 551 - B. BERENSON: 1936, p. 474.

XX

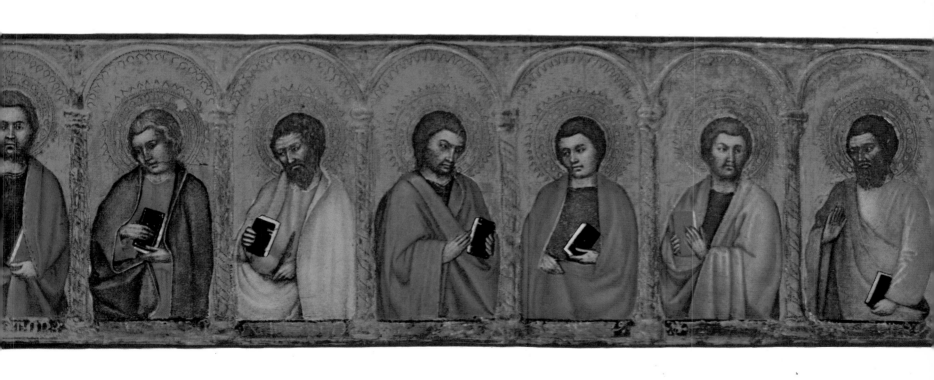

TADDEO DI BARTOLO

Deposition

Panel, 24 × 57 cm.

CONDITION: damaged during the war, and restored by G. Marchig. PROVENANCE: unknown.

" With the death of the Lorenzetti, the Sienese School of painting fell from which it never seriously rallied. It had moments of hopefulness and hours of hectic beauty but never again did it receive that replenishment of force without which art is doomed to dwindle away. Barna, Bartolo di Fredi, and Taddeo di Bartolo at times catch a glow from the splendour of Simone Martini and the Lorenzetti."

B. BERENSON, Italian Painters of the Renaissance, « The Phaidon Press », London, pp. 102-103.

Berenson's attribution of this predella panel to Taddeo di Bartolo is not accepted by some scholars. Despite certain morphological resemblances with Taddeo's images, the painting reveals characteristics of intense rough realism, dry linearism and revival of Duccio-like forms (in the faces of the bystanders) which indicate a different personality.

BIBLIOGRAPHY
B. BERENSON: 1932, p. 55L.

XXI

ANDREA VANNI

Siena, documented from 1353 to 1413

Madonna and Child

Panel, 59 × 46 cm.

CONDITION: good. PROVENANCE: acquired before 1903 from Signor Volpi, Florence.

" Nor did he [Barna], like Giorgione, leave a follower who in great measure could continue his work. Neither Bartolo di Fredi nor even Andrea Vanni were of a measure to succeed him. They merely exploited him; Bartolo, his narrative side alone, and Vanni his inspired sense of the spiritual, his prophetic zest, his ecstasy."

B. BERENSON, *Notes on Tuscan Painters of the Trecento in the Staedel Institut at Frankfurt* « Studies in Medieval Painting », New Haven, 1930, pp. 92-93.

Although Berenson and Mason Perkins had assigned this to Andrea Vanni, the painting was adjudged, according to Langton Douglas, a XVth century work by some Vanni follower better than the master himself. The derivation from Vanni's style is evident, but the dry artisan-like quality of the work is undoubtedly below the Master's usual level.

BIBLIOGRAPHY

F. MASON PERKINS: *Andrea Vanni*, in « The Burlington Magazine », 1903, II, p. 316 (Review by E. MODIGLIANI in « L'Arte », 1903, p. 294 as well as one by G. CAGNOLA in « Rassegna d'Arte », 1903, p. 159) - LANGTON DOUGLAS: *A Note on Recent Criticism of the Art of Sassetta*, in « The Burlington Magazine », 1903, III, p. 275, n. 1 - G. DE NICOLA: *Andrea di Vanni* in « Thieme-Becker » I, 1907, p. 465 - J. A. CROWE, G. B. CAVALCASELLE: *A History of Painting in Italy*, London, 1908, (L. DOUGLAS ed.), III, p. 130 n. - B. BERENSON: *The Central Italian Painters of the Renaissance*, New York-London, 1909, p. 261 - B. BERENSON: 1932, p. 587 - B. BERENSON: 1936, p. 505.

XXII

ANONYMOUS, BYZANTINE STYLE
FIRST HALF OF XIVTH CENTURY

Madonna and Child (half-figure)

Panel, 48 × 25 cm.

CONDITION: good. PROVENANCE: unknown.

Garrison considered this work of possibly Dalmatian origin.

BIBLIOGRAPHY

E. B. GARRISON: *Addenda ad indicem*, II, in «Bollettino d'Arte», October-December 1951, p. 303.

ANONYMOUS, BYZANTINE STYLE
OF XIVTH CENTURY

St. Simeon

Panel, 84 × 42 cm.

CONDITION: good. PROVENANCE: purchased in Florence from Adolfo Melli around 1930.

A work probably by a Venetian-Byzantine artist of the end of the 14th century, or of the first half of the 15th century. In the archaic construction of the modelling, bits of naturalism may be observed; and the ornamentations on the gold background indicate a knowledge of Gothic taste.

BIBLIOGRAPHY
Unpublished.

JACOBELLO DEL FIORE

Venice, documented from 1400 – died 1439

St. Francis

Panel, 94 × 44 cm.

CONDITION: damaged during the war and restored by G. Marchig. PROVENANCE: unknown.

At first, Berenson considered this a youthful work by Gentile da Fabriano. Later, however, he assigned it, though with some hesitation, to the youthful period of Jacobello del Fiore. Perhaps the elements of naturalistic grace and physiognomical intensity of this very beautiful painting induced Berenson to place it in the earliest period of activity of those Masters of the flowery gothic style. Considering that the deep chromatic tonality and graphic definition are certainly archaic in character, and that the severe, frontal, 14th century structure is the dominating feature, we would be inclined to attribute this polyptych panel to a mid-14th century Venetian master. Zeri doubtfully attributes it to Paolo Veneziano.

BIBLIOGRAPHY

B. BERENSON: *The Central Italian Painters of the Renaissance*, New York-London, 1909, p. 174 - J. A. CROWE, G. B. CAVALCASELLE: *A New History of Painting in Italy*, (E. Hutton ed.), London, 1909, III, p. 149, note - B. BERENSON: 1957, I, p. 93.

JACOBELLO DEL FIORE

Madonna and Child

Panel, 56 × 40 cm.

CONDITION: good. PROVENANCE: unknown.

" The most interesting painter of the transition from the Greek Mediaeval style to that of the Italian Renaissance is not represented anywhere in America. This was Jacobello del Fiore, who, in his sumptuous *Justice* of the Venice Academy, in his mighty *Lion* of the Doge's Palace, and in a *Madonna* in my own collection, advances upon his age to a largeness of planes and a succulence of treatment curiously like Palma's."

B. BERENSON, Venetian Painting in America, New York, 1916, p. 5.

BIBLIOGRAPHY

B. BERENSON: *Venetian Painting in America*, New York, 1916, p. 5 - B. BERENSON: 1932, p. 270 - B. BERENSON: 1936, p. 232 - L. COLETTI: *Pittura Veneta del Quattrocento*, Novara, 1953, pp. X, XII - B. BERENSON: 1957, I, p. 93.

MICHELE GIAMBONO

Venice, active from about 1420-1462

St. Michael enthroned

Panel, 113 × 64 cm.

CONDITION: good. PROVENANCE: put on sale in London as " German School " and acquired by J. P. Richter who still owned it in 1895, and then sold it to B. Berenson in 1899.

" The forms, the drawing, and the feeling-elements wherein Giambono is less influenced by Renaissance motifs than any of his mates—justify this ascription, and the colouring—deeper than that of most early Venetian paintings—also points to the mosaicist as its author." (Regarding the *San Marco* of the L. Mond Collection).

B. BERENSON, *The Study and Criticism of Italian Art*, London, 1901, p. 93.

Giambono's masterpiece was perhaps the central panel of a polyptych, whose reconstruction we owe to R. Longhi, and more completely to E. Sandberg-Vavalà. Other works that must have formed part of this polyptych are the *St. John the Baptist* of the Bardini Museum in Florence, the *St. Peter* of the Kress Collection in Washington, the *Saint Gregory the Great* and the *St. Augustine* of the Civic Museum of Padua, the *Saint Mark Reading*, No. 3917, of the National Gallery of London, the *Bishop Saint Martyr* (damaged) of the Civic Museum of Padua, the *Bishop Saint* of the Gardner Museum in Boston and the *St. Stephen* of the Gibert, formerly Frizzoni Collection of Bellagio.

It is datable about 1430. The *St. Michael* perhaps may be the work referred to by Cavalcaselle in the Dondi dell'Orologio collection at Padua, where other panels of the series may be found.

BIBLIOGRAPHY

J. A. CROWE, G. B. CAVALCASELLE: *A History of Painting in North Italy*, London, 1871, I, pp. 295, 296 (cf. T. Borenius, Ed.), London, 1912, vol. I, p. 15 note, vol. II, p. 3 note) - G. FRIZZONI: Review of: L. VENTURI: *Le Origini della Pittura Veneziana*, in « L'Arte », 1907, p. 462 note - B. BERENSON: *The Study and Criticism of Italian Art*, London, 1901, I, p. 93 - J. P. RICHTER: *The Mond Collection*, London, 1910, I, p. 59 - A. VENTURI: vol. VII, 1911, p. 302 - G. Mc N. RUSHFORTH: *Two Pictures by Giambono* in « The Burlington Magazine », 1911-11, XX, pp. 106, 107 - A. S.: *Bibliographical Report of Rushforth's above mentioned Article*, in « L'Arte », 1912, p. 158 - L. TESTI: *La Storia della Pittura Veneziana*, vol. II, Bergamo 1915, pp. 26, 27 - G. FIOCCO: *Michele Giambono*, in « Venezia »; Milan, 1920 - R. VAN MARLE: vol. VII, 1926, p. 367 - vol. VIII, 1927, p. 48, note 3 - G. FIOCCO: *Nota su Jacopo Nerito* in « Rivista d'Arte », XI, 1929, p. 264 - B. BERENSON: 1932, p. 228 - B. BERENSON: 1936, p. 196 - R. LONGHI: *Viatico per Cinque Secoli di Pittura Veneziana*, Florence, 1946, p. 50 - R. PALLUCCHINI: *Tresors de l'Art Vénitien*, Milan-Brussels, 1947, p. 21 - E. SANDBERG-VAVALÀ: *The Reconstruction of a Polyptych by Michele Giambono*, in « Journal of the Warburg and Courtauld Institutes », 1947, p. 22 - W. ARSLAN: *Intorno a Giambono e a Francesco de' Franceschi*, in « Emporium », 1948, pp. 285-289 - L. COLETTI: *Il Maestro degli Innocenti*, in « Arte Veneta », II, 1948, p. 40 - M. DAVIES: *The Earlier Italian School - National Gallery Catalogues*, London, 1951, pp. 175-176 - L. COLETTI: *Pittura.Veneta del Quattrocento*, Novara, 1953, p. XIII - F.M. GODFREY: *Early Venetian Painters 1415-1495*, London, 1954, p. 6 - L. GROSSATO: *Catalogo del Museo Civico di Padova*, Venice, 1957, pp. 62, 63 - B. BERENSON: 1957, p. 82 - L. MAGAGNATO: *Catalogo della Mostra da Altichiero a Pisanello*, Verona-Venice, 1958, p. 71.

St. Catherine of Alexandria and *Martyr Saint with the Cross of St. Andrew*

Two small panels, 45 × 12.5 cm. each.

CONDITION: damaged during the war and restored by G. Marchig. PROVENANCE: unknown.

These small panels, which Berenson assigned to the Catalan School, probably derive from the small pilasters of a polyptych, and are most likely the product of a Valencian Master (in the circle of Marzal de Sas) of the first part of the 15th century. (cf. *Retablo di Santa Barbara* of the Bosch collection, Barcelona, in C. R. Post – *A History of Spanish Painting*, vol. III, 1930, pp. 74 ff.)

BIBLIOGRAPHY
Unpublished.

GENTILE DA FABRIANO

Fabriano, c. 1360 – Rome, 1427

Madonna and Child

Panel, 25 × 19 cm.

CONDITION: fragment, worm-eaten, with flaking of pigment. PROVENANCE: acquired in the antique market at Rome at the beginning of the century.

" Umbrian art reveals itself clearly, if not completely, in its first great master, Gentile da Fabriano. To a feeling for beauty, and a sense for colour nurtured on Sienese models, to a power of construction fostered by contact with Florentine art, Gentile added a glowing vivacity of fancy, and, thus prepared, he devoted his life to recording the Medieval ideal of terrestrial happiness, clear, complete at last (as is the wont of ideals) when the actuality, of which it was the enchanting refraction was just about to fade into the past. "

B. BERENSON, Italian Painters of the Renaissance - « The Phaidon Press », London 1952, p. 115.

This fragment, which Colasanti connects with the Pisa *Madonna*, is dated by Grassi toward 1425, and related to the *Goldman Madonna* in Washington. The same author notes a strong Sienese influence in the work, which is of the same period as the *Madonna* of the A. Saibene collection, Milan.

BIBLIOGRAPHY

F. MASON PERKINS: *La Pittura all'Esposizione d'Arte Antica di Perugia* in « Rassegna d'Arte », 1907, p. 120 - B. BERENSON: *The Central Italian Painters of the Renaissance*, New York-London, 1909, p. 174 - A. COLASANTI: *Gentile da Fabriano*, Bergamo, 1909, p. 60 - B. C. KREPLIN: *Gentile da Fabriano* in « Thieme Becker », XIII, 1920, p. 404 - R. VAN MARLE: vol. VIII, 1927, pp. 18, 22 - B. BERENSON: 1932, p. 221 - B. BERENSON: 1936, p. 190 - L. SERRA: *L'Arte nelle Marche* vol. II, Rome 1934, p. 226 - L. GRASSI: *Tutta la Pittura di Gentile da Fabriano*, Milan, 1953, pp. 32, 61.

GENTILE DA FABRIANO

St. Peter, St. Paul

Two Panels: The *St. Peter* measures 23.8 × 6.5 cm. (width of gold ground: 6.5 cm.)—the *St. Paul*, 23.2 × 8.5 (gold ground: 6.7 cm.).

On the back of the *St. Paul*, reported Degenhart, there is written in a seventeenth century hand: "*Gentile da Fabriano pinxit—fragmento che era nella Cappella overa... sepoltura di casa Sancti nelle (?) orofecerie Anno 1610*" (and in another handwriting) "*cioè dalle parti (dalla panca?) della pala (?) con certi intagli all'antica i quali erano condotti per la longhezza del tempo.*" (According to Volpe: " *... i quali da tarli erano corrotti ...* ").

["*Painted by Gentile da Fabriano—fragment that was in the Chapel or rather... burial ground of the Sancti family in the (?) goldsmith's shop Year 1610*" (and in another handwriting) "*that is, on the sides (on the bench?) of the altarpiece (?) with certain engravings in the old style which were worn out by age.*" (Volpi interprets: "*which were eaten away by termites...*")]

CONDITION: fair, the colours have lost some tone. PROVENANCE: unknown.

Attributed by Berenson to Stefano da Zevio, the two small Saints were assigned by Degenhart to Pisanello. Earlier, Degenhart had accepted the Stefano attribution, relating it with a *St. Anthony Abbot* in the Pisa Museum. The latter work, however, is part of a series to which there also belongs a *St. Jerome* of the Campana collection in the vaults of the Louvre, a work by an Iberian artist active in Tuscany at the time of Starnina (Volpe). The attribution to Gentile, and its connection, as panels of the small pilasters, with the polyptych by Valle Romita now at the Brera, is due to Volpe, and was accepted by Berenson.

BIBLIOGRAPHY

B. BERENSON: *The North Italian Painters of the Renaissance*, New York, London, 1907, p. 302 - B. BERENSON: 1932, p. 550 - B. BERENSON: 1936, p. 472 - B. DEGENHART: *Stefano da Zevio* in «Thieme-Becker», XXXI, 1937, p. 529 - B. DEGENHART: *Di una Pubblicazione su Pisanello e di altri Fatti*, II, in «Arte Veneta», 1954 - C. VOLPE: *Due Frammenti di Gentile da Fabriano* in «Paragone», n. 101, 1958, pp. 53 ff. - I. MAGAGNATO: *Da Altichiero a Pisanello: Catalogo della Mostra di Verona*, Venice, 1958, p. 75 - E. SINDONA: *Pisanello*, Milan, 1961, p. 122.

LORENZO MONACO

Florence, 1370 c. – 1425 c.

Madonna enthroned with St. John the Baptist and St. Zenobius

Panel, 89 × 45 cm.

CONDITION: damaged during the war and restored by G. Marchig. Some repainting and slight flaking of pigment. PROVENANCE: unknown.

" In Lorenzo Monaco we again encounter an artist, not of the highest rank nor of the widest range, but still more worthy of admiration and attention than any that we have had to do with since we left the Orcagnas... Here as in other early efforts,... Lorenzo attempts to get the bulk of Giotto's monumental figures. This is an interesting tendency showing itself after such a lapse of time and just before Masaccio was born, and all the more singular as it appears in the youth of an artist destined in his maturity to devote his best energies to calligraphic draperies and tumultuous effects."

B. BERENSON, *Homeless Pictures – The Fourteenth Century Florentines* (From the author's original manuscript, July 1930, pp. 93-94).

Youthful work which Pudelko dated between the little *Triptych*, No. 157 of the Siena Pinacoteca, and painting No. 1119 of the Berlin Museum, datable 1402 or 1403. Gronau would also date this panel toward 1400. As Brandi and Pudelko have observed, very interesting relationships exist between this *Madonna* and Sienese art, especially Fei, typical of this period of the artist's life.

BIBLIOGRAPHY

B. BERENSON: 1932, p. 299 - B. BERENSON: 1936, p. 257 - G. PUDELKO: *The Stylistic Development of Lorenzo Monaco*, I, in « The Burlington Magazine », 1938, LXXIII, p. 238, n. 12 - H. D. GRONAU: *The Earliest Works of Lorenzo Monaco* in « The Burlington Magazine », XCII, 1950, p. 221.

LORENZO MONACO

Madonna of Humility

Panel, 78 × 42 cm. Inscribed on the base: *Ave Maria — A.D. MCCCCV*.

CONDITION: the surface is very dirty; traces of worm holes. PROVENANCE: from the collection of Aldo Noseda, Milan.

" After designing this masterpiece, [*King David*, formerly at the Cassel Gallery] Lorenzo seems to have fallen more and more subject to the swing and swirl of the late Gothic, which was to die presently like a Bacchante or dervish, exhausted with whirling. I wonder at times whether our artist would have gone so far on this road if all the while he was painting in a resisting and restraining medium like tempera, instead of the more fluid one of illumination. One may be allowed also to believe that the illuminations of choir-books, to which he devoted himself for some time from about 1410 on, may have facilitated the change. Illumination was still being done in the Tuscany of that time with a technique more free, more fluid, more sketchy—more calligraphic in short—than tempera.
It is interesting to note the acceleration of the rhythm in the first of the two homeless Lorenzo Monaco's still to be mentioned. It is very marked in the *Madonna of Humility* that used to be in the Aynard Collection. Better than a tabulated account will be the reproduction of an almost identical *Madonna* painted five or six years earlier, a picture dated 1405 that happens to belong to me. The first is more nervous in action and expression, has more quirks and crotchets in the folds of the draperies, and, in short, is closer to the ultimate goal of calligraphy, the ceremonial penmanship of the Ottoman Turks."

B. BERENSON, *Homeless Pictures - The Fourteenth Century Florentines* (from the author's original manuscript, July 1930, pp. 96-97).

In addition to being a very important work in tracing out Lorenzo Monaco's stylistic development, this panel is also one of his most beautiful productions, its vivacious human intensity harmonizing with the measured rhythms of the linear arabesque as well as with the well-scanned plastic placement within the given space.

BIBLIOGRAPHY

O. SIRÉN: *Don Lorenzo Monaco*, Strassbourg, 1905, p. 38 - B. BERENSON: *The Florentine Painters of the Renaissance*, New York-London, 1909, p. 204 - V. LAZAREFF: *Una Madonna di Lorenzo Monaco a Mosca* in « L'Arte », 1924, XXVII, pp. 124 ff. - R. VAN MARLE: vol. IX, 1927, pp. 127, 130 - P. TOESCA: *La Pittura Fiorentina del Trecento*, Verona, 1929, p. 67, n. 34 - B. BERENSON: *Quadri senza Casa - Il Trecento Fiorentino*, IV in « Dedalo », 1932, I, p. 32 - B. BERENSON: 1932, p. 299 - B. BERENSON: 1936, p. 257 - G. PUDELKO: *The Stylistic Development of Lorenzo Monaco*, I, in « The Burlington Magazine », LXXIII, 1938, p. 238, n. 13.

ANDREA DI GIUSTO

Florence, active first half of XVth C. – died 1455

Madonna and Child enthroned, under a canopy. In the cusp: *Dove of the Holy Spirit.*

Panel, 121 × 71 cm. The base of the frame bears the inscription: *AVE MARIA GRATIA PLENA DOMINUS TECUM. MCCCCXXXV.*

CONDITION: fair, with traces of overpainting. PROVENANCE: unknown.

"As for Andrea, he seems to have been one of those journeymen artisans who are ready for any employment. He was always of the opinion of his last employer, and within the circle of his disabilities, did his best to imitate him. Thus, he imitated Lorenzo Monaco, and Masaccio and Masolino and Fra Angelico and perhaps even humbler but successful artists like Giovanni del Ponte. But he remained always rather uncertain, rather flimsy and rather blurred."

B. BERENSON, *Homeless Pictures - The Fifteenth Century Florentines.* (From the author's original manuscript, July 1930, p. 6).

This *Madonna*, which Berenson assigned to Andrea di Giusto, reveals the strong influence of Fra Angelico together with Masolinesque elements.

BIBLIOGRAPHY
Unpublished.

XXXIII

DOMENICO VENEZIANO

Born : Venice, documented from 1438 - died: Florence 1461

Madonna and Child

Panel, 86 × 61.5.

CONDITION: good. PROVENANCE: acquired by B. Berenson 16 April 1900 from Marchesa Marianna Panciatichi Ximenes Paulucci (Gallery Panciatichi, Florence. Listed as No. 59). EXHIBITIONS: " Exposizione della Società delle Belle Arti ", Florence 1900.

" The force of this influence [Domenico Veneziano over Alessio Baldovinetti] betrays itself elsewhere, up to the end of Alessio's career, in one trait and another. In all his *Madonnas* that we know, he follows Domenico's type with a fidelity even greater than that of any of this master's accredited pupils. It would be hard to find a resemblance so close between any work of Piero dei Franceschi's and his master Domenico Veneziano, as we may descry between a *Madonna* by Alessio belonging to the present writer, and Domenico's *Madonna* in the Uffizi. (Note 1: This *Madonna*, until it came into the author's possession, passed for Piero dei Franceschi's. I shall not attempt here to substantiate my conviction that it is Baldovinetti's, nor, perchance, will it be necessary, if I succeed in persuading the reader that the Louvre picture is by him. Yet the resemblance to Veneziano is so great that more than one critic has seriously held it to be his.) "

B. BERENSON, - The Study and Criticism of Italian Art II, London, 1902, p. 32.

Despite Cavalcaselle's published attribution (1864) of this work to Domenico Veneziano, (an attribution supported by Bode, Supino and Weisbach) the work was subsequently listed in the Panciatichi collection under Piero della Francesca. Berenson, and later Venturi, assigned it to Baldovinetti. In his 1932 " Lists ", however, Berenson accepted the Domenico attribution, and since that time, no other scholars have taken up the problem. While Pudelko affirms that this *Madonna* is inspired by the marble Madonna attributed to Pagno di Lapo in the Museum of the Opera del Duomo, Florence, Salmi maintains that the compositional scheme has been derived from Fra Angelico's altarpiece in San Domenico, Fiesole.

Fiocco considers it the most primitive of Domenico's *Madonnas*. Pudelko would place it a little before the London *Madonna* which he dates toward 1455. Salmi, on the other hand, dated it a little after 1440. Finally, Berti considers a dating about 1436, a little earlier than that which he proposed for the Carnesecchi *Madonna*, London. Undoubtedly created before the altarpiece of St. Lucia dei Magnoli (c. 1440) and with touches of courtly Gothic flowery ornamentation, the work might be placed during the years 1435-1438.

BIBLIOGRAPHY

J. A. CROWE, G. B. CAVALCASELLE: *Storia della Pittura in Italia*, Florence, 1892, vol. V, p. 134 - W. BODE: *Aus der Berliner Gemäldegalerie. Eine Predellatafel von Domenico Veneziano*, in « Jahrbuch der Preuss. Kunstsamml. », IV, 1883, pp. 89 ff. - B. BERENSON: *The Florentine Painters of the Renaissance*, New York-London, 1900, p. 103 - I. A. SUPINO: *Esposizione di alcune Opere di Arte Antica* in « L'Arte », 1900, p. 313 - W. WEISBACH: in « Jahrbuch der Preuss. Kunstsamm. », XXII, 1891, p. 38 - B. BERENSON: *The Study and Criticism of Italian Art*, London, 1902, vol. II, pp. 23 ff. - B. BERENSON: *The Florentine Painters of the Renaissance*, New York-London, 1909, p. 110 - A. BELLINI PIETRI: *Di due Tavole del Ghirlandaio nel Museo Civico di Pisa*, in « Bollettino d'Arte », 1909, p. 332 - B. BERENSON: *Italian Paintings - Catalogue of a Collection of Paintings and Some Art Objects*, J. G. Johnson, Philadelphia, 1913, p. 18 - G. GRONAU: *Domenico Veneziano* in « Thieme-Becker », IX, 1913. p. 409 - R. LONGHI: *Un Frammento della Pala di Domenico Veneziano per Santa Lucia de' Magnoli* in « L'Arte », 1925, p. 33 - R. OFFNER: *Italian Primitives at Yale University*, New Haven, 1927 - R. VAN MARLE: vol. X, 1928, pp. 324 ff. - vol. XI, 1929, pp. 267, 280 n. 2 - B. BERENSON: 1932, p. 172 - B. BERENSON: *Fra' Angelico, Fra Filippo e la Cronologia*, in « Bollettino d'Arte », 1932, p. 5 - B. TOESCA: *Domenico da Venezia* in « Enciclopedia Italiana Treccani », XIII, 1932, p. 118 - G. PUDELKO: *Studien über Domenico Veneziano* in « Mitteilungen des Kunsthistorischen Institutes in Florenz », 1934, IV, p. 180 - B. BERENSON: 1936, p. 148 - M. SALMI: *Paolo Uccello, Andrea dal Castagno, Domenico Veneziano*, Milano, 1936 (2nd ed., 1938) pp. 85, 175, note a plate 194 - R. W. KENNEDY: *Alessio Baldovinetti*, New Haven, 1938 - G. FIOCCO: *La Pittura Toscana del Quattrocento*, Novara, 1941, p. XVI - B. BERENSON, 1952, plate 155 - G. PACCAGNINI: *Una Proposta per Domenico Veneziano* in « Bollettino d'Arte », XXXVII, 1952, p. 118 - C. SEMENZATO: *Un'Opera Giovanile di Domenico Veneziano*, in « Rivista d'Arte », XXIX, 1954. - L. BERTI: *Catalogo della Mostra di Quattro Maestri del Primo Rinascimento*, Florence, 1954, p. 81 - L. BERTI: *Domenico Veneziano* in « Enciclopedia Universale dell'Arte », IV, 1958, p. 402.

XXXIV

WORKSHOP OF FRANCESCO PESELLINO

Florence, mid XVth C.

Madonna and Child with two Angel musicians

Panel: 70 × 52 cm.

CONDITION: damaged during the war and restored by G. Marchig. PROVENANCE: unknown.

" Still another type of Madonna, this time with angels, must have been designed by
Pesellino if we may judge from surviving versions and echoes.
Readers should discount prejudice in favour of my own belongings, but I cannot help
finding my own version more satisfactory than any other. Here the composition is
one of the most successful pyramidal ones that had been designed up to date. The
Madonna of Humility sits low on a cushion and two child angels at her feet make music.
The types, the peculiarities of every kind, the colour, all point to an original by Pesellino himself, and to the panels in question as a studio version. None of the variants
known to me are as happy."

B. BERENSON, *Homeless Pictures - The Fifteenth Century Florentines.* (From the author's original manuscript, July 1930, pp. 34-35).

According to Offner, the creator of this *Madonna* is a Florentine artist of the workshop of the Codex Vir-
giliano miniature in the Riccardiana Library, Florence (therefore called " Virgil Master "). Offner also
attributes to the same workshop a group of painted chests, as well as a group of *Madonnas* such as No. 30
of the Fogg Art Museum, Cambridge (USA), catalogued under the School of Boccati, but recognized
in the 1919 catalogue as by the same painter who had created the *Berenson Madonna*. The " Virgil
Master " group in part unites the works which Schubring formerly assigned to the " Dido Master ", and
Venturi to the Master of the Jarves Cassoni (cf. B. Berenson, *Italian Paintings of the Renaissance*, 1932
p. 346). In 1929, Salmi implemented the group of " Virgil Master" *Madonnas* by including among them
the *Virgin with Angel-Musicians* of the Dreyfus Collection, Paris. Berenson associates the Dreyfus Virgin with the same group of workshop copies from Pesellino originals, among which he would include
the *Madonna* in his own possession, the *Madonna and Angels* (formerly Toscanelli) and the *Fogg Madonna*.

BIBLIOGRAPHY

CATALOGUE: *Collection of Medieval and Renaissance Paintings*, Fogg Art Museum, Harvard University, Cambridge 1919, p. 155 - B. BERENSON: 1932,
p. 442 - B. BERENSON: *Quadri senza Casa - Il Quattrocento Fiorentino*, II, in « Dedalo », 1932, I, p. 679 - B. BERENSON: 1936, p. 380 - R. OFFNER:
Italian Primitives at Yale University, New Haven, 1927, p. 27 - R. VAN MARLE: X, 1928, p. 552.

XXXV

MASTER OF THE CASTELLO NATIVITY

mid XVth C. Florentine

Madonna and Child

Panel, 65 × 42 cm.

CONDITION: restored by G. Marchig. PROVENANCE: unknown.

" As suggested in the J. G. Johnson catalogue, where this painter was first isolated and integrated, the " Castello Master ", as we shall call him for short, descended from Fra Angelico, and wound his way between Fra Filippo and Baldovinetti. Also, as I have since learned, he must have owed more than a little to Domenico Veneziano and finally as we see in his *Annunciation* at St. Giovanni dei Cavalieri, Florence, he was attracted into the orbit of the still youthful Botticelli."

B. BERENSON, *Homeless Pictures - The Fifteenth Century Florentines*. (From the author's original manuscript, July 1930, p. 56).

Despite damage resulting from over-painting, the high quality of this work is evident. The composition is certainly inspired by a Domenico Veneziano prototype.

BIBLIOGRAPHY

B. BERENSON: *Italian Painting - A Catalogue of a Collection of Paintings, etc.*, I, Philadelphia, 1913, p. 19, n. 23 - R. VAN MARLE: vol XI, 1929, p. 300 - B. BERENSON: 1936, p. 279.

NERI DI BICCI

Florence, 1419 c. - died after 1491

Nativity

Predella panel, 26.5 × 100 cm.

CONDITION: fair. The panel has been cradled. PROVENANCE: acquired in Florence, 1924, from G. Volterra.

" ... Neri di Bicci, who, if he was not the most popular painter in Florence—and for all we know he was—ran the busiest picture-factory in a community where, through a long career he was the contemporary of nearly all the artists who have made Florentine painting great. The son and pupil of a popular painter, he fell under the influence of Fra Angelico, Fra Filippo, Domenico Veneziano and Pesellino. There he stopped, unlike his Venetian equivalent Lazzaro Sebastiani, who could not resist imitating recognized talent even when it might be embodied in men youthful enough to be his grandsons, his great grandsons almost. And unlike this wooden Venetian uncouthly hopping after the youngsters, Neri, although his types are ugly, his compositions rudimentary, his colouring hot, is never stupid and seldom dull. There is a whimsicality, a heartiness, a candour about him that win one over. And yet, and yet—that this should have been the painter whom part of the community at least loved to honour when the whole galaxy of universal genius from Pollaiuolo to Botticelli, to Leonardo, to Perugino, to Signorelli, had well passed their meridian! What a warning to be cautious in deciding what was the character of a period, and what were its popular currents."

B. BERENSON, *Homeless Pictures - The Fifteenth Century Florentines* (From the author's original manuscript, July 1930, pp. 65-66).

We do not know the complex to which this delightful predella, typical of the mature art of Neri di Bicci, belonged.

BIBLIOGRAPHY

R. VAN MARLE: vol. X, 1928, p. 540 - B. BERENSON: 1932, p. 386 - B. BERENSON: 1936, p. 332 - H. KIEL: note in « Du », December 1957.

Madonna and St. Lawrence in adoration of the Child

Panel, 60 × 46 cm.

CONDITION: damaged during the war; colours are dirty and grainy; the panel is warped and cracked. Restored by G. Marchig. PROVENANCE: unknown.

In this typical work, Neri di Bicci reveals his ingenuous grace, expressing the new form-language of the Renaissance in terms of an archaicizing iconography.

BIBLIOGRAPHY
B. BERENSON: 1932, p. 386 - B. BERENSON: 1936, p. 332.

XXXVIII

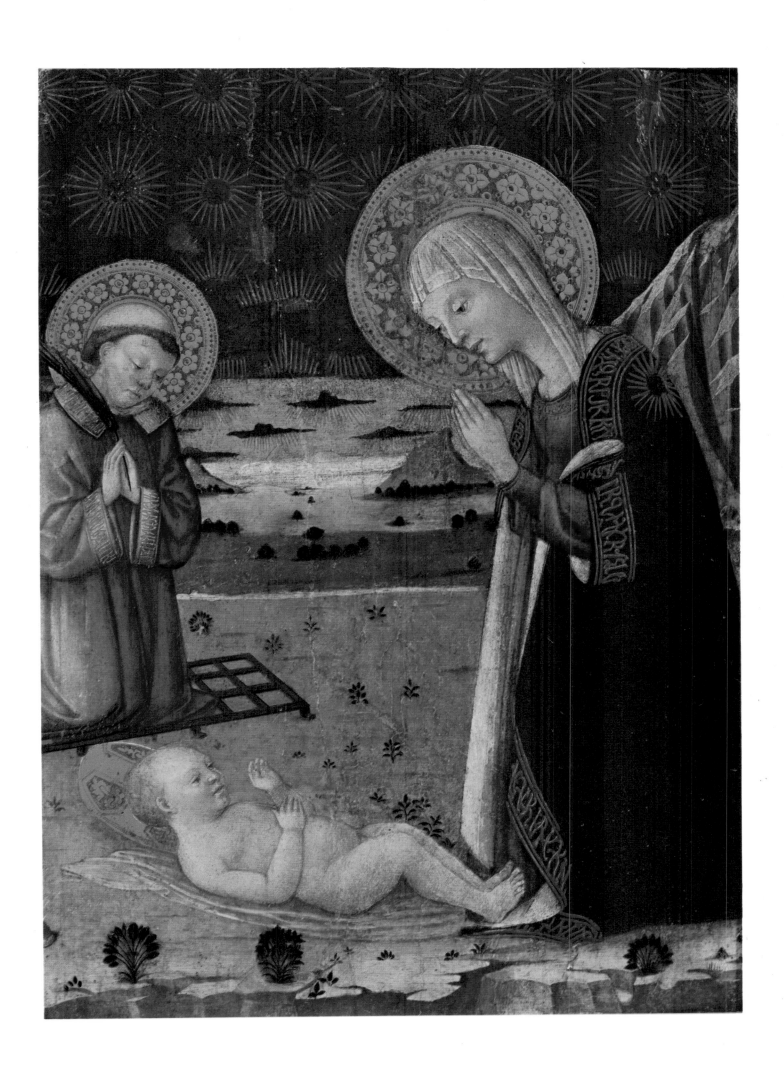

FLORENTINE MASTER
OF THE XVᵀᴴ CENTURY, FOLLOWER OF NERI DI BICCI

Annunciation - in the predella: *Presentation of the Virgin, Martyr, Nativity, Bishop Saint with Donor, Birth of Virgin.*

Panel, 119 × 162 cm. predella included.

CONDITION: damaged during the war, and restored by G. Marchig. PROVENANCE: unknown.

" ... If we could be transported to the Florence of toward 1450 we should quite likely discover that, except a few revolutionary artists in their studios and a handful of humanists and enlightened patrons who frequented them, ... The substantial burgher lined with fat capon went on ordering his paintings from the practitioners of the good old school. Giovanni dal Ponte, Mariotto di Nardo, Lorenzo di Niccolò, Rossello di Jacopo Franchi, Francesco d'Antonio Banchi, Bicci di Lorenzo, etc., either direct followers of Lorenzo or influenced by him, were kept busy, ... "

B. BERENSON, Homeless Pictures - The Fourteenth Century Florentines (from the author's original manuscript).

The creator of this work, about whom Zeri is re-uniting a *corpus* of frescoes in the Tuscan countryside, is a contemporary rather than follower of Neri di Bicci. Developing from a phase of academic gothicizing, the artist reveals a stylistic passage toward a flowering of motives in the style of Lorenzo Monaco parallel with the activity of Bicci di Lorenzo.

BIBLIOGRAPHY
Unpublished.

STEFANO DI GIOVANNI CALLED SASSETTA

Cortona or Siena, 1392 (?) – Siena, 1450

St. Francis in Ecstasy; St. John the Baptist; Blessed Ranieri Rasini

Panels of a Polyptych: central, 190 × 122 cm.; laterals, 179 × 58 each.

CONDITION: cracks and some slight flaking. PROVENANCE: the church of San Francesco at Borgo Sansepolcro commissioned the polyptych from Sassetta on 5 September 1437 and the work was duly consigned on 5 June 1444. Removed from the altar in 1752, and remaining in the monastery up to 1810, it was then acquired by Cavalier Sergiuliani of Arezzo who gave it to the Canon Angelucci. The Canon took the polyptych apart, giving one section to his brother, Don Pietro Antonio Montelucci, prior of Monte Contieri. The three panels of the Berenson collection, which were at that time attributed to Piero della Francesca or to Fra Angelico, subsequently became part of the Lombardi and Baldi collection in Florence, where they were seen toward 1855-60 by Cavalcaselle, and later passed into the Toscanelli collection, also in Florence. In fact, they are mentioned in the catalogue of the Toscanelli sale in 1883. Berenson acquired them in Florence, it seems from a cabinetmaker, toward 1902. (with regard to the other parts of the polyptych, see M. Davies, 1951 and E. Carli, 1951 and 1957).
The central panel with *St. Francis in Ecstasy* bore, at the base of the frame, this inscription, subsequently lost: *Cristoforus Francisci Fei e Andreas Johannis Tanis Operarius A. MCCCCXXXXIIII* (cf. G. Rosini in *Storia della Pittura Italiana*, I, plate L, 1839); the date and names of the vestrymen correspond with the documents of the contract.
DOCUMENTATION: Contract dated 5 September 1437 for the polyptych by Stefano di Giovanni commissioned by the church of San Francesco at Borgo Sansepolcro (c.f. M. Davies, *Catalogue of Italian Painting at the National Gallery of London*, 1951, pp. 438 ff.
Document dated 5 June 1444 with regard to the consignment of the polyptych to the church (c.f. Borghesi and Banchi in *Nuovi Documenti per la Storia dell'Arte Senese*, 1898, pp. 142 ff.).

" Over the sea and the land, into the golden heavens towers the figure of the blessed Francis, his face transfigured with ecstasy, his arms held out in his favourite attitude of the cross, his feet firmly planted on a prostrate warrior, in golden panoply. Cherubim and seraphim with fiery wings and deep crescent haloes form behind the saint a nimbus enframing a glory of gold and azure, as dazzling as the sky, and as radiant as the sun. Overhead, on opalescent cloudlets, float Poverty in her patched dress, looking up with grateful devotion, Obedience in her rose-red robe with a yoke about her neck and her hands crossed on her breast, and Chastity in white, holding a lily. Underfoot, beside the crowned knight in armour, obviously symbolising Violence, we see corresponding to Poverty a nun in black holding a press and money-bag, with a watch-dog by her side, as obviously representative of Avarice; and corresponding to Chastity, a pretty woman in purplish rose colour, luxuriously reclining against a black pig, and gazing into a mirror—clearly the Flesh. The almost childlike simplicity of the arrangement, the crimson and gold and azure, the ecstatic figure of the saint, the girlish figures of the radical Franciscan virtues, the more material figures of the vices, the flaming empyrean, the silvery green sea growing lighter as it approaches the silvery grey land, combine to present a real theophany, the apotheosis of a human soul that has attained to complete harmony with the soul of the universe by overcoming all that is belittling and confining, and opening itself out to all the benign influences of the spirit. "
" The Baptist is a tall, emaciated but firm figure, with face of wild enthusiasm and great eloquence. He wears a skin and a long rose-pink mantle draped over his arms, and he carries a slender blue cross. Rainieri is a more monkish figure, with short grey

hair, and grey habit, and a face resembling the Saint's companion in the Mystic Marriage. In his hand he holds a small hoop around which are placed circlets edgewise. "

" The colour, where it has not darkened, or rubbed off, is singularly pure, deep, and transparent. The quasi-mechanical stamping and ornamentation, and the materials employed, alone suffice to make these panels objects of visual pleasure. The drawing is no less pure and delicate than the colouring, and masterly enough not only to suffice for all the exquisite action contained in this series, but to command considerable qualities of structure. "

B. BERENSON, A Sienese Painter of the Franciscan Legend. J. M. Dent & Sons, London, 1910, pp. 39-40-51-52.

According to E. Carli's reconstruction, the Pentatych of St. Francis at Borgo Sansepolcro must have been made up as follows: in front, *Madonna enthroned with six musician angels* (now at the Louvre); *Blessed Ranieri Rasini* (Berenson collection), *St. Anthony of Padua* (Louvre). On the back, center; *St. Francis in Ecstacy* (Berenson collection), and at the sides, on two levels, eight stories from the life of the Saint (seven in the National Gallery, London; one at the Condé Museum, Chantilly). Of the predella, only a *Story of the Blessed Ranieri Rasini*, at the Berlin Museum, has been preserved and from the crown a *St. Francis in Adoration before the Crucifix*, shown at Stuttgart, in 1950 (cf. K. Bauch, in *Festschrift zum 60. Geburtstag von C. G. Heise*, 1950, pp. 103 ff.). Another two panels that were part of the polyptych have recently been recognized by F. Zeri in the vaults of the Pushkin Museum, Moscow, and have been published in the last catalogue, under numbers 1494 and 1496. Perhaps they were cusps, like the Stuttgart panel, while a St. Christopher of the Perkins Collection, also attributed by Zeri, was probably part of the pilasters.

BIBLIOGRAPHY

E. ROMAGNOLI: *Bibliografia Cronologica de' Bellartisti Senesi*, manuscript in the Municipal Library of Siena, vol. IV - G. ROSINI: *Storia della Pittura Italiana*, Pisa, vol. I (1839), plate L, vol. III (1841), p. 20 - S. BORGHESI, L. BANCHI: *Nuovi Documenti per la Storia dell'Arte Senese*, Siena, 1898, pp. 119, 142 - L. COLESCHI: *Storia della Città di Sansepolcro*, 1886, p. 169 - G. MILANESI: *Catalogue de la Collection Toscanelli de Florence*, Florence, 1883 p. 29, n. 112 - G. MILANESI: *Nuovi Documenti per la Storia dell'Arte Toscana*, 1901, pp. 80 ff. - B. BERENSON: *A Sienese Painter of the Franciscan Legend* in « The Burlington Magazine », 1903, VII, VIII, p. 2 ff. pp. 171 ff. - LANGTON DOUGLAS: *A Note on Recent Criticism of the Art of Sassetta*, in « The Burlington Magazine », 1903, pp. 265 ff. - F. MASON PERKINS: *Un Quadro Sconosciuto del Sassetta*, in « Rassegna d'Arte », 1904, pp. 76 ff. - R. L. DOUGLAS: *Sassetta* in « Bryan's Dictionary of Painters and Engravers », V, London, 1905 - L. COLETTI: *Arte Senese*, Treviso, 1906 - E. JACOBSEN: *Das Quattrocento in Siena*, Strasbourg, 1908 - B. BERENSON: *The Central Italian Painters of the Renaissance*, New York-London, 1909, p. 245 - B. BERENSON: *A Sienese Painter of the Franciscan Legend*, London, 1909 - F. SCHOTTMUELLER: *Sassetta's Gemälde : die Messe des hl. Franziskus* in « Berliner Museen: Berichte aus den Preuss. Kunstsamm. », XXXI, Berlin, 1909-10 - M. LOGAN BERENSON: *Il Sassetta e la Leggenda di S. Antonio Abate* in « Rassegna d'Arte », 1911, pp. 202 ff. - A. VENTURI: vol. VII, part I, Milan, 1911, p. 494 - E. BERTAUX: *Le Musée Jacquemart-André* in « Revue de l'Art Ancien et Moderne », XXIV, 1913 - J. A. CROWE, G. B. CAVALCASELLE: *A New History of Painting in Italy* (E. Hutton ed.), London, 1909, III, p. 121 - L. DAMI: *Siena e le sue Opere d'Arte*, Florence, 1915 - L. GIELLY: *Le Sassetta* in « L'Art et les Artistes ». NS. I, Paris, 1919-20 - P. ESCHER: *Die Malerei der Renaissance in Italien*, I, Berlin, 1922 - W. BODE: *Ein Neuerworbenes Gemälde Sassettas in Kaiser Friedrich Museum*, in « Berliner Museen: Berichte aus den Preuss. Kunstsamm. », XIV, Berlin, 1924 - E. HUTTON: *The Sienese School in the National Gallery*, London, 1925 - T. BORENIUS: *Some Franciscan Subjects in Italian Art*, in « St. Francis of Assisi: Essays in Commemoration », London, 1926 - R. VAN MARLE: vol. IX, 1927, p. 348 - R. LONGHI: *Piero della Francesca*, Rome, 1927 - T. BORENIUS: *Pictures from American Collections at Burlington House*, in « Apollo », 1930, XI - L. KERN: *Le Bienheureux Rainier de Borgo San Sepolcro*, in « Revue d'Histoire Franciscaine », 1930, p. 282 - B. BERENSON: 1932, p. 511 - G. EDGELL: *A History of Sienese Painting*, New York, 1932, p. 193 - M. L. GENGARO: *Il Primitivo del Quattrocento Senese : Stefano di Giovanni detto Sassetta* in « La Diana », VIII, 1933, pp. 18, 26 - L. VENTURI: *Italian Paintings in America*, New York, Milan, 1933 - M. SALMI: *Paolo Uccello, Domenico Veneziano, Piero della Francesca e gli Affreschi del Duomo di Prato*, in « Bollettino d'Arte », XXVIII, 1934, p. 23 - K. CLARK: *Seven Sassettas for the National Gallery*, in « The Burlington Magazine », LXVI, 1935 - F. MASON PERKINS: *Sassetta* in « Thieme Becker », XXIX, 1935 - B. BERENSON: 1936, p. 440 - J. POPE HENNESSY: *Sassetta* London, 1939, pp. 98, 102, 105, 106, 130, 131, 164 - R. LONGHI: *Fatti di Masolino e Masaccio*, in « La Critica d'Arte », V, 1940, XXV-XXVI - E. CARLI: *Capolavori dell'Arte Senese*, Florence, 1946, p. 41 - B. BERENSON: *Sassetta*, Florence, 1946 - C. BRANDI: *Quattrocentisti Senesi*, Milan, 1949, pp. 58 ff. - R. OERTEL: *Frühe Italienische Tafelmalerei*, Catalogue of the Stuttgart Exhibition, 1950, p. 55 - K. BAUCH: *Christus am Kreuz und der Heilige Franziskus*, in « Festschrift zum 60. Geburtstag von C. G. Heise », Berlin, 1950 pp. 103 ff. - R. LONGHI: *Primitivi Italiani a Stoccarda*, in « Paragone », 7, Florence, 1950 - H. D. GRONAU: *Early Italian Painting at Stuttgart* in « The Burlington Magazine », XCII, 1950, p. 322 - E. CARLI: *Sassetta's Borgo San Sepolcro Altarpiece* in « The Burlington Magazine », XCIII, 1951, p. 145 - M. DAVIES: *The Earlier Italian Schools - National Gallery Catalogues*, London, 1951, pp. 390 ff. - G. KAFTAL: *Iconography of the Saints in Tuscan Painting*, Florence, 1952, pp. 405, 884 - E. SANDBERG-VAVALÀ: *Sienese Studies*, Florence, 1953, pp. 233, 246 - E. CARLI: *La Pittura Senese*, Milan, 1955, p. 196 - G. C. ARGAN: *De Van Eyck à Botticelli*, Geneva, 1955 - E. CARLI: *Sassetta e il Maestro dell'Osservanza*, Milan, 1957, pp. 50 ff., 126.

STEFANO DI GIOVANNI CALLED SASSETTA

Apostles taking leave of the Virgin

Panel, 27.5 × 40 cm. On the back, written in Russian: *Transferred from wood to canvas 1870 by A. Suvorov.*

CONDITION: the transfer was skilfully executed. PROVENANCE: the small picture passed from a Russian collection to the B. Crespi collection, Milan. Acquired by B. Berenson from Mr. Zen, Milan, after 1914.

"[The Asciano Altarpiece] ... is a triptych representing the birth of the Blessed Virgin. But for its greater sense of beauty, greater dignity of pose, greater suavity of expression, and greater gorgeousness and flatness of colour, the subject is treated as it might have been by a Rogier van der Weiden or a Memling. It is a domestic scene carried out with that sense of every little action and every little circumstance having an almost sacramental value, the indispensable precision of ritual, which sense it is the sole business of justifiable *genre* painting to communicate."

B. BERENSON, A Sienese Painter of the Franciscan Legend, London, 1909, p. 56.

" ... I never felt happy about the attribution to Sassetta [of the Asciano polyptych and that of the Osservanza of 1436] and now in the light of better acquaintance with the Master I must eliminate them altogether ... Let me add parenthetically that for the present I leave them unfathered, unable as I am to attach them to any artistic personality, although obviously of the group centering around Sassetta."

B. BERENSON, Sassetta, (Italian Edition 1946), note p. 52.

In the Benigno Crespi collection, the work was attributed to Fra Angelico. It was Berenson himself who re-attributed it to Sassetta. Pope-Hennessy had already related it to the triptych of Asciano, as the left part of the predella, the center of which had been identified by the same scholar in the *Pietà* of the Dijon Museum.

The present panel, as well as the complex wherein it originally played a part, was mentioned by Longhi (1940) in the list of works to be subtracted from the *corpus* of Sassetta. These works composed the nucleus for the reconstruction of that personality to whom Graziani gave the name " Maestro dell'Osservanza ", developing and clarifying previous attemtps to distribute among various artists (such as the " Pseudo Pellegrino di Mariano " and the " Vatican Master ") all the works which had previously been entirely attributed to Sassetta.

The attribution to the " Maestro dell'Osservanza was accepted by Carli, Laclotte and Salvini. The Asciano-Osservanza group and other works of Graziani's list, were assigned instead by Brandy, Pope-Hennessy and Berenson to the young Sano di Pietro, an attribution which, however, had previously been decisively rejected by Graziani, Longhi and Carli. Therefore, we may assume that Berenson—although he had never explicitly spoken of the panel, but expressed the view that the entire Asciano polyptych should be attributed to Sano di Pietro—would have subsumed the painting under this name in a new edition of his " List."

The dating of the Asciano altarpiece, generally considered earlier than 1436, (when the Osservanza polyptych was completed) was changed toward 1438 by Carli, who supported this later date with valid arguments.

BIBLIOGRAPHY

B. BERENSON: *Scoperte e Primizie Artistiche* in «Rassegna d'Arte», August 1904, p. 126 - E. JACOBSEN: *Das Quattrocento in Siena*, Strassbourg 1908, p. 26 - B. BERENSON: *The Central Italian Painters of the Renaissance*, London-New York, 1909, p. 246 - M. SALMI: *Un Dipinto del Sassetta* in «La Diana», 1927, pp. 52 ff. - R. VAN MARLE: vol. IX, 1927, pp. 361 ff. - F. MASON PERKINS: *Sassetta* in «Thieme-Becker», 1935, p. 482 - B. BERENSON: 1932, p. 512 - M. L. GENGARO: *Il Primitivo del Quattrocento Senese: Stefano di Giovanni detto il Sassetta*, in « La Diana », VIII, 1933, pp. 16, 25 - B. BERENSON: 1936, p. 440 - J. POPE-HENNESSY: *Sassetta*, London, 1939, pp. 63, 66, 67, 80, 82, 90 - R. LONGHI: *Fatti di Masolino e Masaccio* in « La Critica d'Arte », 1940, p. 188, n. 26 - A. GRAZIANI: *Il Maestro dell'Osservanza*, in « Proporzioni », II, 1948, p. 75 - E. CARLI: *Capolavori dell'Arte Senese*, Florence 1946, p. 46 - J. POPE-HENNESSY: *The Literature of Art - Proporzioni II*, in «The Burlington Magazine», 1948, p. 359 - C. BRANDI: *Quattrocentisti Senesi*, Milan, 1949, pp. 73, 254 note - G. KAFTAL: *Iconography of the Saints in Tuscan Paiñting*, Florence, 1952, p. 405 - E. CARLI: *La Pittura Senese*, Milan, 1955, p. 206 - M. LACLOTTE: *De Giotto à Bellini, Catalogue of the Paris Exhibition*, 1956, p. 70 - J. POPE-HENNESSY: *Rethinking Sassetta* in «The Burlington Magazine», XCVIII, 1946 - E. CARLI: *Sassetta e il Maestro dell'Osservanza*, Milan, 1957, pp. 90, 100, 130 - R. SALVINI, L. TRAVERSO: *Predelle dal '200 al '400*, Florence, 1959, pp. 91 ff.

SANO DI PIETRO

Siena, 1406-1481

Madonna nursing Child

Panel, 52.5 × 38.5 cm.

CONDITION: fair. PROVENANCE: unknown.

" ... young Sano di Pietro, like so many other followers of creative artists, was not capable, left to himself, of maintaining the level which he had achieved under the Master's [Sassetta's] direction. "

B. BERENSON, Epilogue to *Sassetta* (from the author's original manuscript).

Berenson included this panel among the " Maestro dell'Osservanza " group, that is, one of those Sassetta-like works which he considered youthful products of Sano di Pietro, directly influenced by the Master, and hence of a much higher quality than Sano's later works.

BIBLIOGRAPHY

F. MASON PERKINS: *Ancora dei Dipinti Sconosciuti della Scuola Senese, II*, in « Rassegna d'Arte Senese », 1908, I, p. 7 - E. GAILLARD: *Sano di Pietro*, Chambéry, 1923 p. 196 - E. TRUBNER: *Die Stilistische Entwicklung der Tafelbilder des Sano di Pietro*, Strassbourg, 1925 - B. BERENSON: 1932, p. 499 - B. BERENSON: 1936, p. 429.

SANO DI PIETRO

Madonna and Child, two Angels with Saints Jerome and Bernardino.

Panel, 57 × 43 cm.

CONDITION: good. PROVENANCE: acquired through Signor Paolini.

" ... the most monotonous, the most spiritless, the most vapid of them all, Sano di Pietro ..."

B. BERENSON, Homeless Pictures – The Fifteenth Century Sienese (from the author's original manuscript. July 1930, p. 5).

This is one of Sano's graceful variations on a theme which certainly met with public favour. Trübner dates the work 1456 or 1457.

BIBLIOGRAPHY

F. MASON PERKINS: *Alcuni Dipinti Senesi Sconosciuti o Inediti* in « Rassegna d'Arte », 1913, p. 123 note 2 - E. GAILLARD: *Sano di Pietro*, Chambéry, 1923, p. 196 - E. TRÜBNER: *Die Stilistische Entwicklung der Tafelbilder des Sano di Pietro*, Strassbourg, 1925 - R. VAN MARLE: vol. IX, 1927, p. 512 - B. BERENSON: 1932, p. 499 - M. SALMI: *Dipinti Senesi nella Raccolta Chigi-Saracini* in « La Diana », VIII, 1933, p. 82 - C. BRANDI: *La R. Pinacoteca di Siena*, Rome, 1933, p. 261 - B. BERENSON: 1936, p. 429.

PIETRO DI GIOVANNI AMBROSI

Siena, 1410-1449

Madonna of the pomegranate

Panel, 74 × 48 cm.

CONDITION: good. PROVENANCE: unknown.

" The angels in the Cortona picture [of Sassetta] recall a panel in the writer's possession which deserves mention here. The Virgin is seen behind a parapet on which she supports the Child. One of her hands touches His shoulder, while the other holds a pomegranate. Two angels rest their arms on the ledge, and two others, in long robes, rise high above. Unfortunately, no reproduction gives an adequate idea of this work, partly because much of its beauty depends on its colour. The tender devoutness of the angels does not suffice, in the mere black and white, to overcome the bad construction of the Madonna's head and the too primitive drawing of the Child. But the rose mauve of the Virgin's dress, as well as of the lower angels, the pale blue of her mantle, the very dark greenish blue of the upper angels' robes, sewn with golden crosses, the fiery red and gold of their wings, the crimson diadems, the yellow hair, combined with the design, not only produce an effect of hieratic gorgeousness, but at the same time exhale a subtle perfume of pre-Raphaelitism—I mean something of that perfume which Rossetti conveys both in his verse and in his painting."

B. BERENSON, *A Sienese Painter of the Franciscan Legend*, J. M. Dent, London, 1910, pp. 60-61.

" To him [Pietro di Giovanni Ambrosi] I would now attribute with some hesitation the *Madonna with Angels* in my own collection."

B. BERENSON, *Sassetta* (from the author's original manuscript, p. 7).

Originally attributed by Berenson to Sassetta and accepted as such by Van Marle, Jacobsen and Gengaro the painting was subsequently reattributed by Berenson himself to Pietro di Giovanni Ambrosi.

Pope-Hennessy considers it the work of a student of the Sassetta-like painter whom he named " Maestro Castelli Mignanelli "; and dating it around 1450, makes it the eponymous work of a " Master of the Berenson Madonna ". Brandi also rejected the Ambrosi attribution, dating the work at least a decade after that artist's death.

The similarities with Ambrosi seem rather external, and the fine painting might perhaps find a better attribution among artists from the Marches.

BIBLIOGRAPHY

B. BERENSON: *A Sienese Painter of the Franciscan Legend*, in « The Burlington Magazine », 1903, VIII, pp. 171 ff. - E. JACOBSEN: *Das Quattrocento in Siena*, Strassbourg, 1908 - B. BERENSON: *The Central Italian Painters of the Renaissance*, New York-London, 1909, p. 245 - B. BERENSON: *A Sienese Painter of the Franciscan Legend*, London, 1909 - R. VAN MARLE: vol. IX, 1927, p. 340 - G. EDGELL: *A History of Sienese Painting*, New York, 1932, plate 270 - M. L. GENGARO: «*Il Primitivo del Quattrocento Senese: Stefano di Giovanni detto il Sassetta*», in «La Diana», VIII, 1933, p. 31 - B. BERENSON: 1932, p. 458 - B. BERENSON: 1936, p. 393 - J. POPE-HENNESSY: *Sassetta*, London, 1939, p. 171 - C. BRANDI: *Quattrocentisti Senesi*, Milan, 1949, p. 226 n. - J. POPE-HENNESSY: in « The Art Bulletin » 1951, p. 142 - G. COOR: *Neroccio De' Landi*, Princeton, 1961, pp. 46, 67 - E. CARLI: *Pittura Senese*, Milan, 1961.

GIOVANNI DI PAOLO

Siena, c. 1399–1482

Madonna of Humility

Panel, 54 × 32 cm.

CONDITION: good. PROVENANCE: acquired in Paris, 1910, from L. A. Rosenberg.

" ... It has something of the heartiness and winsomeness of that quaint master, quaint but in many respects incorrigibly Byzantine, and at times deserving the nickname of the " Greco of the Sienese Quattrocento."

B. BERENSON, *Homeless Pictures – The Fifteenth Century Sienese* (from the author's original manuscript, p. 5).

Dated between 1426 and 1445 by Pope-Hennessy, and between 1440 and 1445 by Brandi, this work with its severe controlled expressionism is typical of the artist's maturity.

BIBLIOGRAPHY

F. MASON PERKINS: *Dipinti Senesi Sconosciuti o Inediti* in « Rassegna d'Arte », 1914, p. 165 n. I - O. SIRÉN-C. H. WEIGELT: voce *Giovanni di Paolo* in « Thieme Becker », XIV, 1921, p. 123 - R. VAN MARLE: vol. IX, 1927, pp. 390, 451 n. 2 - F. MASON PERKINS: *Pitture Senesi Poco Conosciute* in « La Diana », I, 1931, p. 29 (reprinted in « Pitture Senesi », Siena, 1933, p. 62) - B. BERENSON: 1932, p. 246 - M. L. GENGARO: *Giovanni di Paolo* in « La Diana », 1932, p. 22 - G. H. EDGELL: *A History of Sienese Painting*, New York, 1932, p. 217 - B. BERENSON: 1936, p. 211 - J. POPE-HENNESSY: *Giovanni di Paolo*, London, 1937, p. 34 - C. BRANDI: *Giovanni di Paolo* in « Le Arti », 1941, No. V, p. 327 note - C. BRANDI: *Giovanni di Paolo*, Florence, 1947.

XLV

LORENZO DI PIETRO CALLED VECCHIETTA

Siena, documented from 1428 - died 1480

PROCESSIONAL CROSS, front: *Christ on the Cross, Mary Magdalen, God the Father, Mary, John* - back: *Christ on the Cross, the four Evangelists.*

Panel, 44 × 37 cm.

CONDITION: good. PROVENANCE: unknown.

" The most remarkable of Sassetta's followers is yet to be mentioned. It was Lorenzo Vecchietta, the wonderful sculptor, delightful painter, and maker of three out of the four real artists with whom native Sienese art closes its story, I mean Francesco di Giorgio, Neroccio di Landi, and Benvenuto di Giovanni."

B. BERENSON, A Sienese Painter of the Franciscan Legend, London, 1909, p. 69.

Vigni has correctly dated this lovely processional cross as about 1445. Coor maintains that it was painted in Vecchietta's workshop with the collaboration of his student, Neroccio.

BIBLIOGRAPHY

F. MASON PERKINS: *Ancora dei Dipinti Sconosciuti della Scuola Senese*, in « Rassegna d'Arte Senese », 1908, p. 9 - J. A. CROWE, G. B. CAVALCASELLE: *A New History of Painting in Italy*, (E. Hutton ed.), London, 1909, III, p. 110 note - G. VIGNI: *Lorenzo di Pietro detto il Vecchietta*, Florence, 1937, p. 74 - F. MASON PERKINS: «Thieme-Becker», XXXIV, 1940, p. 155 - G. COOR: *Neroccio De' Landi*, Princeton, 1961, pp. 18, 41.

MATTEO DI GIOVANNI

Borgo San Sepolcro, c. 1430 – Siena, 1495

Madonna and Child, Saints Jerome, Catherine and five Cherubim

Panel, 68.5 × 43 (without frame)

CONDITION: poor. PROVENANCE: acquired from G. B. Brauer, in Paris, 1910.

" Matteo had a feeling for movement which would have led to real art if he had had the necessary knowledge of form; lacking this, he became an inferior Crivelli, giving us effects of firm line cut in gilt cordovan or in old brass."

B. BERENSON, Italian Painters of the Renaissance – (The Phaidon Press, London 1952, p. 103).

Typical work of the artist's maturity, datable 1480 and influenced by the art of Neroccio.

BIBLIOGRAPHY

F. MASON PERKINS: *Due Quadri Inediti di Matteo di Giovanni* in « Rassegna d'Arte Senese », 1907, p. 37 - E. JACOBSEN: *Das Quattrocento in Siena*, Strassbourg, 1908, p. 64 note - B. BERENSON: *The Central Italian Painters of the Renaissance*, New York-London, 1909, p. 195 - F. HARTLAUB: *Matteo da Siena und seine Zeit*, Strassbourg, 1910, p. 77 - F. MASON PERKINS: *Matteo di Giovanni* in « Thieme-Becker », XXIV, 1930, p. 256 - B. BERENSON: 1932, p. 351 - M. L. GENGARO: *Matteo di Giovanni* in « La Diana », 1934, p. 177 - B. BERENSON: 1936, p. 302 - R. VAN MARLE: vol. XVI, p. 332 - P. BACCI: *Fonti e Commenti per la Storia dell'Arte Senese*, Siena, 1944, p. 244 - G. COOR: *Neroccio De' Landi*, Princeton, 1961, p. 123.

MATTEO DI GIOVANNI

Bust of Saint (St. Philip Benizzi?)

Panel, 38.5 × 31.5 cm. A label on the back bears the inscription: " *Bartolommeo Vivarini. L. 3000.*"

CONDITION: good. Slight flaking of pigment. PROVENANCE: unknown.

" Matteo, who was from Borgo Sansepolcro, would have perhaps become a great Florentine if chance had taken him, as it had taken his fellow townsman, Piero della Francesca, to Florence. Chance took him to Siena and there his energetic temperament and his inquiring mind succumbed to the ecstasy that Siena demanded from its painters, and his baffled and frustrated spirit took its revenge in depicting the *Massacre of the Innocents* with the caricatured vehemence and savage ferocity of a Spaniard or a German. Once and once only did he yield himself up wholeheartedly to Siena, and then he created one of the most fascinating works of the whole Quattrocento, the *Assumption* in the London National Gallery."

B. BERENSON, *Homeless Pictures - The Fifteenth Century Sienese* (from the author's original manuscript, July 1930, pp. 13-14).

Pope-Hennessy has advanced the theory that this very beautiful *Bust of a Saint* was part of the superstructure of the pilasters of the Altarpiece by Matteo di Giovanni, formerly in S. Agostino at Asciano, a work of 1474, whose central panel would be the *Assumption of the Virgin*, No. 1155 of the National Gallery of London. He would also consider, as part of this work, the *St. Augustine* and the *St. Michael* of the Siena Pinacoteca, and the *Annunciation* of the R. Lehman collection, New York, and the *Annunciating Angel* (very damaged) placed on the antique market in New York in 1924—26. The hypothesis is entirely acceptable.

BIBLIOGRAPHY

F. MASON PERKINS: *Ancora dei Dipinti Sconosciuti della Scuola Senese* in «Rassegna d'Arte Senese», 1908, p. 4 - E. JACOBSEN: *Das Quattrocento in Siena*, Strassbourg, 1908, pl. XXX - B. BERENSON: *The Central Italian Painters of the Renaissance*, New York-London, 1909, p. 195 - G. F. HARTLAUB: *Matteo da Siena und seine Zeit*, Strassbourg, 1910, p. 141 - F. MASON PERKINS: *Alcuni Dipinti Senesi Sconosciuti o Inediti* in «Rassegna d'Arte», 1913, p. 198 - B. BERENSON: 1932, p. 351 - M. L. GENGARO: *Matteo di Giovanni* in «La Diana», 1934, pp. 172, 175 - B. BERENSON: 1936, p. 302 - R. VAN MARLE: vol. XVI, 1937, p. 346 - J. POPE-HENNESSY: *Matteo di Giovanni's Assumption Altarpiece* in «Proporzioni», III, 1950, pp. 82, 85 n. 15 - M. DAVIES: *The Earlier Italian Schools - National Gallery Catalogues*, London, 1951, p. 287.

GUIDOCCIO COZZARELLI

Siena, 1450–1516

St. Monica praying for the conversion of St. Augustine

Panel 41 × 38 cm.

CONDITION: the pigment is dirty and in danger of flaking. PROVENANCE: unknown.

" ... it must not be assumed that whenever we encounter spidery extremities, uncertain contours, and even more uncertain modelling in a picture ascribed to Matteo (di Giovanni) we are justified in shouting: ' This is by Guidoccio Cozzarelli.' Not a bit of it. This pupil of Matteo's has a distinct personality of his own, and there is no reason why we should throw at him everything that we take away from his master."

B. BERENSON, *Homeless Pictures – The Fifteenth Century Sienese* (from the author's original manuscript. July 1930, pp. 15-16).

Zeri has correctly connected this panel with two others, depicting *The Vision of St. Augustine* and *The Flagellation of a Saint* in the Ryerson collection, Chicago, attributed to Matteo di Giovanni, and datable 1482. The minor dimensions of the Berenson panel might be the result of a mutilation, or else this is an end panel of the predella. (The Ryerson panels, once in the collection of Lord Brownlow, London, were exhibited at the Burlington Club in 1904, catalogue nos. 38 and 43—Cf. L. Venturi, *Italian Pictures in America*, Van Marle, XVI, 1937, p. 342 and Berenson, 1936, p. 301).

BIBLIOGRAPHY

B. BERENSON: *The Central Italian Painters of the Renaissance*, New York-London, 1909, p. 159 - F. MASON PERKINS: in « Rassegna d'Arte Senese », 1911, p. 20 - G. DE NICOLA: *Guidoccio Cozzarelli*, in « Thieme Becker », VII, 1913, p. 38 - B. BERENSON: 1932, p. 157 - B. BERENSON: 1936, p. 136 - R. VAN MARLE: vol. XVI, 1937, p. 378.

FRANCESCO DI GIORGIO MARTINI

Siena, 1439-1502

Scene near Temple

Panel, 41 × 53 cm.

CONDITION: good. PROVENANCE: the work was acquired in 1912 from a Tuscan church by the photographer Burton. It was completely covered by a 17th century oil painting, depicting *Christ at the Sepulcher*. Under the darkened layer of the ground, Herbert Horne discerned the sharp lines of architecture. A thorough cleaning revealed the original painting, which was then purchased by Berenson who attributed it to Francesco di Giorgio.

" ... that most fascinating of Sienese quattrocentists..."

B. BERENSON, *Homeless Pictures - The Fifteenth Century Sienese* (from the author's original manuscript, p. 21).

Perkins interpreted the subject of this fragment of a cassone panel as an episode in the slaying of Penelope's suitors by Ulysses, or, according to Misciatelli's theory, as the abduction of Helen by Paris.

BIBLIOGRAPHY

F. MASON PERKINS: *Dipinti Senesi Sconosciuti o Inediti*, in «Rassegna d'Arte», 1914, n. 5, p. 104, note I - P. SCHUBRING: *Cassoni*, Leipzig, 1915, p. 135 and Supplement, 1923, p. 5 n. 937 - A. MC. COMB: *The Life and Works of Francesco di Giorgio*, in «Art Studies» 1924, pp. 14, 15, 21 - P. MISCIATTELLI: *Cassoni Senesi* in «La Diana», year IV, issue 2, 1929, p. 122 - L. VENTURI: *Italian Paintings in America*, New York - F. MASON PERKINS: *Pitture Senesi Poco Conosciute* in «La Diana», 1931, p. 30 (reprinted in «Pitture Senesi», Siena, 1933, p. 63) - G. H. EDGELL: *A History of Sienese Painting*, New York, 1932, p. 243 - S. BRINTON: *Francesco di Giorgio*, 1934-35, vol. I, p. 110 - B. BERENSON: 1932, p. 202 - B. BERENSON: 1936, p. 174 - R. VAN MARLE: vol. XVI, pp. 257, 286 (1937) - A. S. WELLER: *Francesco di Giorgio Martini*, Chicago, 1943, pp. 112-115 ff. - R. PAPINI: *Francesco di Giorgio Architetto*, Florence, 1946, vol. I, p. 353, vol. II, plate 5 - B. BERENSON: 1952, plate 274 - E. CARLI: *La Pittura Senese*, Milan, 1955, p. 256 - G. COOR: *Neroccio De' Landi*, Princeton, 1961, pp. 25, 27.

L

FRANCESCO DI GIORGIO MARTINI

Group of youths under a portico

Panel, 34.5 × 27.5 cm.

CONDITION: The panel is a fragment. The picture is dirty and deteriorated. PROVENANCE: unknown.

" There was, however, still another link between the Sienese and Tura, Cossa and Ercoli. The last were essentially the product of that extraordinary archaeological, scientific and naturalistic movement at Padua connected with the name of Squarcione. Another product of the same movement, Girolamo da Cremona, appeared in the Sienese as early as 1467, and remained there long enough to leave a marked impression upon all the abler painters of that region, but on none so much as on Matteo."
" ... In Berlin a *predella* by Girolamo (No. 1655) representing the *Healing of the Cripple* is catalogued as " Manner of Francesco di Giorgio "... their attribution is a tribute to the influence exercised by the Cremonese upon Cecco di Giorgio."

B. BERENSON, Essays in the Study of Sienese Painting, New York, 1918, p. 68, note.

Berenson, Van Marle, Weller and Pope-Hennessy attributed this work to Francesco di Giorgio; and it was dated between 1480 and 1490 by Pope-Hennessy who connected it with the *Chess Match* of the Metropolitan Museum of New York and the *Scene* of the Wauthers collection, Brussels. However, Zeri attributes this painting, as well as the others—all parts of a single work—to Gerolamo da Cremona. Longhi, instead, assigns the group to Liberale da Verona, and his judgment is accepted by Laclotte.

BIBLIOGRAPHY

A. MC COMB: *The Life and Works of Francesco di Giorgio*, in « Art Studies », Harvard Princeton, II, 1924, pp. 3 ff. - B. BERENSON: 1932, p. 202 - B. BERENSON: 1936, p. 174 - R. VAN MARLE: vol. XVI, 1937, p. 274 n. 3 - A. S. WELLER: *Francesco di Giorgio Martini*, Chicago, 1943, p. 235 - J. POPE-HENNESSY: *Sienese Quattrocento Painting*, London, 1947, p. 32 - F. ZERI: *Una Pala d'Altare di Gerolamo da Cremona*, in « Bollettino d'Arte », 1950, p. 39 - R. LONGHI: *Un Apice Espressionistico di Liberale da Verona*, in « Paragone », 1955, n. 65, p. 3 - M. LACLOTTE: *De Giotto à Bellini - Catalogue de l'Exposition*, Paris, 1956, p. 61.

NEROCCIO DI BARTOLOMEO LANDI

Siena, 1447 - 1500

Saints Dominick, Francis and Bonaventura (or Benedict) appearing before St. Catherine of Siena

Panel, 39 × 28 cm.

CONDITION: good. Restored by A. Vermehen. PROVENANCE: acquired in London, 1911 from Dowdeswell and Dowdeswell.

A very beautiful youthful painting wherein the luminous and chromatic type of Albertiana architecture provides a fitting setting for Sienese narrative charm. Particularly noteworthy is the landscape framed in the doorway with cypresses beyond the columns of the portico—touches reminding us of Domenico Veneziano.
A panel of the *Mystic Marriage of St. Catherine*, from the R. W. Christiansen collection, was put on sale by Sotheby's in London on 14 June 1961 (cf. illus. cat. p. 43). Both the Berenson and Christiansen panels derive from the same work, inspired by Giovanni de Paolo's Pizzicaiuoli altar (1447-1449).

BIBLIOGRAPHY

F. MASON PERKINS: *Pitture Senesi Poco Conosciute* in « La Diana », 1931, p. 30 (reprinted in « Pitture Senesi », Siena, 1933, p. 63) - B. BERENSON: 1932, p. 390 - B. BERENSON: 1936, p. 335 - R. VAN MARLE: vol. XVI, 1937, p. 312 n. 3 - G. KAFTAL: *St. Catherine of Siena in Tuscan Painting*, 1949, p. 38 - G. KAFTAL: *Iconography of the Saints in Tuscan Painting*, Florence, 1952, p. 235 - G. COOR: *Neroccio De' Landi*, Princeton, 1961, pp. 19, 22, 24, 25, 166.

NEROCCIO DI BARTOLOMEO LANDI

Madonna and Angels with Saints Jerome and Anthony of Padua

Panel, 88 × 51 cm.

CONDITION: good. PROVENANCE: Nevin collection, Rome, acquired between 1895 and 1906.

" As for Neroccio—why, he was Simone come to life again. Simone's singing line, Simone's endlessly refined feeling for beauty, Simone's charm and grace—you lose but little of them in Neroccio's panels, and you get what to most of us counts more, ideals and emotions more akin to our own, with quicker suggestions of freshness and joy."

B. BERENSON, *Italian Painters of the Renaissance* – « The Phaidon Press », London, 1952, p. 103.

Typical work of the artist's youth, dated by Dami at about·1476.

BIBLIOGRAPHY

F. MASON PERKINS: *Su Certi Quadri Sconosciuti di Neroccio* in « Rassegna d'Arte Senese », 1906, n. 3, p. 83 - E. JACOBSEN: *Das Quattrocento in Siena*, Strassbourg, 1908, p. 84 - B. BERENSON: *The Central Italian Painters of the Renaissance*, New York-London, 1909, p. 206 - P. ROSSI: *Neroccio di Bartolomeo Landi e la sua più grande Tavola* in « Rassegna d'Arte Senese », 1909, V, p. 27 note - F. MASON PERKINS: *Alcuni Dipinti Senesi Sconosciuti o Inediti* in « Rassegna d'Arte », 1913, p. 124 - L. DAMI: *Neroccio di Bartolomeo Landi*, in « Rassegna d'Arte », 1913, p. 143 - J. A. CROWE, G. B. CAVALCASELLE: *A History of Painting in Italy*, (ed. L. Douglas and T. Borenius), London, V, 1914, p. 159 n. 6 (Borenius) - G. EDGELL: *A History of Sienese Painting*, New York, 1932, p. 248 - B. BERENSON: 1932, p. 389 - B. BERENSON: 1936, p. 335 - R. VAN MARLE: vol. XVI, 1937, p. 296 - J. POPE-HENNESSY: *The Development of Realistic Painting in Siena*, in « The Burlington Magazine », LXXXIV-V, 1944, p. 144 - G. COOR: *Neroccio De' Landi*, Princeton, 1961, pp. 54 ff., 165.

BENVENUTO DI GIOVANNI DEL GUASTA

Siena, 1436-1518 c.

Dead Christ supported by two Angels

Panel, 34 × 45 cm.

CONDITION: good. PROVENANCE: acquired at the Cherami sale where it was catalogued as a work of Alvise Vivarini. It had also been attributed, in the past, to Carlo Crivelli.

" ... the Olivetan Order which had great houses in Milan and Verona was responsible for the presence in Sienese territory of various artificers from the Valley of the Po, and among them of Girolamo da Cremona and Liberale da Verona. These illuminators brought with them a certain breath of Padua, and just a whiff they succeeded in passing on to their Sienese contemporaries. It makes itself felt in an unusual incisiveness of outline, and an unusual preference for bright scarlets and blues such as we find in Matteo, but even more in Neroccio, and most of all in Benvenuto di Giovanni.
This may account for the fact that the last named artist's earlier and better works, when found away from Siena, were apt to be attributed to " Squarcionesque " painters. A well known panel with the story of the Passion in the Cook collection at Richmond passed for a Montagna. At the Cherami sale, where I got the *Pietà* now in my own collection, it was catalogued as an Alvise Vivarini."

B. BERENSON, - *Homeless Pictures - The Fifteenth Century Sienese* (from the author's original manuscript, July 1930, pp. 17-18).

Central panel of a predella from the youthful period of the artist.

BIBLIOGRAPHY

F. MASON PERKINS: *Due Dipinti Senesi della Pietà*, in «Rassegna d'Arte Senese», VII, 1911, p. 67 - M. SALMI: *Gerolamo da Cremona Miniatore e Pittore*, II, in «Bollettino d'Arte», 1922/23, vol. I - P. ROSSI: *Le Antiche Pitture della Pietà nel Palazzo del Monte dei Paschi*, in «Rassegna d'Arte Senese», XVIII, 1925, p. 15 - B. BERENSON: *Quadri senza Casa - Il Quattrocento Senese*, I, in «Dedalo», 1930/31, vol. III, p. 643 - L. M. TOSI: *Benvenuto di Giovanni* in «Enciclopedia Italiana Treccani», VI, 1930, p. 660 - B. BERENSON: 1932, p. 76 - B. BERENSON: 1936, p. 66 - R. VAN MARLE: vol. XVI, 1937, p. 407 - G. COOR: *Neroccio De' Landi*, Princeton, 1961, p. 203.

GIROLAMO DI BENVENUTO

Siena, 1470-1524

Madonna appearing to the Patrician John and his wife

Panel, 37 × 32 cm.

CONDITION: good. PROVENANCE: formerly in the Prince Orloff-Demidoff collection, Paris. Acquired by B. Berenson through Trotti and Co., Paris, 1911, as a work of Benvenuto di Giovanni.

" Girolamo has a certain dignity and elegance of his own, but shows from the start a tendency to woodenness."

> B. BERENSON, *Homeless Pictures – The Fifteenth Century Sienese* (from the author's original manuscript, July 1930, p. 19).

One of the predella panels from the Altarpiece of the *Madonna of the Snows*, a work dating from 1508, formerly in the Sozzini chapel of San Domenico, Siena. Della Valle makes mention of the predella as being in the Casa Sozzini in 1782; and in 1811, the Abbot Carli said that the Altarpiece had been brought by the Sozzini to the country. Although the Altarpiece passed, in 1890, to the Institute of Fine Arts of Siena and thence to the Pinacoteca, the predella was dispersed. Brandi has attributed other panels besides this one to the predella; specifically, that of the *Miracle of the Snows* (formerly in the Bony collection, Paris, now in the R. Longhi collection, Florence) and that of the *Foundation of Santa Maria Maggiore* (Graham collection, Detroit). Zeri subsequently identified the panel in the *Appearance of Mary before the Pope* in the collection of Mrs. Margareth Drey, London.

Formerly attributed to Benvenuto di Giovanni, the painting was re-attributed by Berenson as a work of Girolamo di Benvenuto, and as such it was named by Mason Perkins who, however, interpreted the scene as a *Miracle of St. Nicholas*. Later, Perkins and also Berenson felt that the small panel represented an *Appearance of the Virgin to Beato Lucchese and his wife*."

BIBLIOGRAPHY

DELLA VALLE: *Lettere Senesi sopra le Belle Arti*, Venice 1782 and Rome 1785, III, p. 58 - A. CARLI: *Notizie Manoscritte*, 1811, (Biblioteca Comunale di Siena), C. VII, 110 p. 146 - F. MASON PERKINS: *Alcuni Dipinti Senesi Sconosciuti o inediti* in « Rassegna d'Arte », 1913, p. 199, n. 4 - F. MASON PERKINS: *Pitture Senesi Poco Conosciute* in « La Diana », VI, 1931, p. 31 (republished in « Pitture Senesi », Siena, 1933, p. 64) - B. BERENSON: 1932, p. 252 - B. BERENSON: 1936, p. 217 - R. VAN MARLE: vol. XVI, 1937, p. 421 - C. BRANDI: *Quattrocentisti Senesi*, Milan, 1949, p. 274 note.

GIOVANNI BOCCATI

Camerino – documented between 1445 and 1480

Madonna and Child adored by two Angels in prayer and two offering vases of flowers

Panel, 84 × 55 cm.

CONDITION: good. PROVENANCE: acquired from Colnaghi, London.

" Earlier in this article we compared the scientific, naturalistic, archaelogical artists to souls in purgatory. Following out the comparison, Boccatis and his kindred the world over may well be described as souls in limbo. They are innocent, they are attractive; they do not distress us with the sight of struggle and strife, failure and filth. They will never grow up. They remain children, and when no longer quite that, they amuse and touch us as do crétins of the Val d'Aosta..."

" Boccatis never outgrew the Transitional pre-scientific stage of painting so delightfully represented in the North by the Limbourgs and their followers, the painters of Cologne, and in the South by Gentile da Fabriano, Pisanello, and their numerous peers and pupils. Only that Boccatis, who, although he lived to about 1480, never showed the least comprehension of the New Age, could not help picking up some of its by-products..."

B. BERENSON, *Essays in the Study of Siense Painting*, New York, 1918, pp. 71, 72.

Typical work of the artist's second period in the Marches, between 1458 and 1470. Francesco Santi would place the painting between the *Platt Madonna* and that of the National Museum of Poznan (oral comm.)

BIBLIOGRAPHY

A. VENTURI: *Studi sull'Arte Umbra del 1400*, in « L'Arte », 1909, p. 190 - B. BERENSON: *The Central Italian Painters of the Renaissance*, New York-London, 1909, p. 153 - J. A. CROWE, G. B. CAVALCASELLE: *A New History of Painting in Italy*, (E. Hutton ed.), London, 1909, III, p. 157 note - W. BOMBE: *Giovanni Boccati*, in «Thieme Becker», 1910, p. 153 - B. FELICIANGELI: *Sulla Vita di G. B. da C., Pittore del Secolo Decimoquinto*, Sanseverino, 1906 - A. VENTURI: vol. VII, 1911, p. 520 - U. GNOLI: *Pittori e Miniatori nell'Umbria*, Spoleto, 1923, p. 161 - B. BERENSON: 1932, p. 90 - A. COLASANTI: *Die Malerei des XV. Jhd. in den Italienischen Marken*, 1932 - L. SERRA: *L'Arte delle Marche*, Rome, 1934, pp. 287 ff. - R. VAN MARLE: vol. XV, 1934, p. 17 n. 2 - B. BERENSON: 1936, p. 78 - S. A. CALLISEN: *The Evil Eye in Italian Art*, in «The Art Bulletin», XIX, 1937, p. 459 n. - B. BERENSON: 1952, plate 293 - M. LACLOTTE: *De Giotto à Bellini - Catalogue de l'Exposition*, Paris, 1956, p. 39.

GIOVANNI BOCCATI

Marriage of the Virgin

Panel, 20.5 × 60 cm.

CONDITION: the colour is dirty. PROVENANCE: formerly in the Charles Butler collection of London with an attribution to Fra Angelico; in that of G. C. Somervales, 1887. Acquired by B. Berenson in London, 1911 from Dowdeswell and Dowdeswell. EXHIBITIONS: New Gallery of London, 1893-94.

" The *Sposalizio* is even more interesting, because the subject lends itself, as a composition, to a design almost identical with the *Meeting of Solomon and the Queen of Sheba*. Boccatis is here not only fresh and attractive but in every way a more modern artist than he is elsewhere. No wonder this panel used to be attributed to the school of Angelico, for the high priest and the Virgin vaguely recall that great and exquisite artist, and much else in the composition suggests Florence. The architecture shows Boccatis in his most advanced phase and so does the drawing. And nevertheless it is rustic simplicity itself, candid, naive, and unambitious, when considered in the light of all the scientific, naturalistic and archeological problems the author of our *Salver* sets himself and solves."

B. BERENSON, Essay in the Study of Sienese Painting 1918, pp. 73-74.

At the Casa Colonna in Rome, Zeri discovered another three panels of the predella of which this constituted the central section. These panels were a *Birth of the Virgin* (left panel) and two figures of *Kneeling Donors* which must have been the end panels. The reintegration has been accepted by Longhi and Meiss. The attribution of these panels which, according to Meiss, probably must have formed the predella of an *Annunciation* is very controversial. While Berenson accepted and supported the attribution to Boccati, Meiss assigned it to the " Master of the Aranci Cloister " and not without reason sensed in it an echo of the *Marriage of the Virgin* frescoed by Domenico Veneziano in St. Egidio, and later destroyed. Zeri, however, decisively rejects such an attribution; he is disposed, rather, to accept Longhi's suggestion of assigning the work to a Florentine Master of the Pollaiuolesque circle about 1465. At the same time, Zeri does not rule out the possibility of " a probable connection with the Marches ", as an old inscription on the back of the Colonna panel, referring to Fra' Carnevale, would seem to indicate.
The interpretation of Florentine stylistic elements, as well as the precise references to the predella of the Altarpiece of Santa Lucia de' Magnoli, noted by Meiss, strike me as having been achieved under the stylistic influence of artists from the Marches who left Florence toward the middle of the 15th Century.

BIBLIOGRAPHY

B. BERENSON: *Essays in the Study of Sienese Painting*, New York, 1918, pp. 73 ff. - B. BERENSON: 1932, p. 90 - R. VAN MARLE: vol. XV, 1934, p. 17 n. 2 - B. BERENSON: 1936, p. 78 - R. LONGHI: *Il Maestro di Pratovecchio*, in « Paragone », n. 35, 1952, p. 34, n. 12 - M. MEISS: *Mortality among Florentine Immortals*, in « Art News », LVIII, 1959, p. 56 - F. ZERI: *Due Dipinti, la Filologia e un Nome, Il Maestro delle Tavole Barberini*, Turin, 1961, p. 52 and n. 1 - M. MEISS: *Contributions to two Elusive Masters*, in « The Burlington Magazine », 1961, pp. 57 ff.

BENEDETTO BONFIGLI

Perugia, documented from 1445 – died 1496

Nativity

Panel, 54 × 41 cm.

CONDITION: good. PROVENANCE: formerly Sterbini collection. Acquired by B. Berenson in Paris, 1910, from G. Brauer.

" As an artist, Bonfigli scarcely ranks as high as Niccolò da Foligno, his fellow—pupil under Benozzo Gozzoli. He was a much more dependent person, but being more imitative, with the models of Fra Angelico or Benozzo before him, he at times painted exquisite things, and by nature he was gifted with that sense of the charming wherewith Perugia was later to take the world captive. Some of the freshest and loveliest of all angel faces may be seen in Bonfigli's altar-pieces and standards. His colour has almost always that hint of gold which never fades from Umbrian art. But far was it from him to harbour a feeling, no matter how faint, for what in painting is more essential than charming faces and pretty colour: and no degenerate Sienese ever was more garrulous and incompetent than Bonfigli when he attempted historical composition. "

B. BERENSON, *Italian Painters of the Renaissance* - « The Phaidon Press », London, 1952, p. 117.

The work might be dated about 1455, at the time of the beginning of the frescoes in the Chapel of the Priors at Perugia. The refined stylization of the slender figures, nature conceived of as a courtly green-house, indicate how Bonfigli renders the formal elements of the new Florentine Masters in an exquisitely Gothic spirit.

BIBLIOGRAPHY

A. VENTURI: *La Galleria Sterbini in Roma*, Rome, 1906, pp. 145 ff. - U. GNOLI: *Pittori e Miniatori nell'Umbria*, 1923, p. 349 - B. BERENSON: 1932, p. 93 - R. VAN MARLE: vol. XIV, 1933, p. 104 - B. BERENSON: 1936, p. 80 - B. BERENSON: 1952, pl. 299.

FRANCESCO DI GENTILE DA FABRIANO

Marches, active from 1460 to 1480 c.

Annunciation

Panel, 175 × 137 cm.

CONDITION: damaged during the war and restored by G. Marchig. There has been a great deal of repainting, and much flaking of pigment. PROVENANCE: unknown.

" In Mr. Berenson's *Annunciation* the arrangement betrays the influence of Verrocchio, and the grandiose arch and columns, contact with architects like Luciano Laurana or the young Bramante."

B. BERENSON, *Italian Painting - A Catalogue of a Collection of Paintings*, etc., J. G. Johnson, Philadelphia, 1913, Vol. I, p. 76.

The work, in which Serra discerned Umbrian, Verrocchio-like characteristics, does not seem,—in view of its frank roughness, its plastic force and power of design—to fit very well into the definitely established group of works by Francesco di Gentile.

BIBLIOGRAPHY

B. BERENSON: *Italian Painting - A Catalogue of a Collection of Paintings*, etc., J. G. Johnson Philadelphia, 1913, p. 76 - THIEME-BECKER: *Francesco di Gentile*, XII, 1916, p. 303 - L. SERRA: *Francesco di Gentile da Fabriano*, in « Rassegna Marchigiana », XI, 1939, pp. 80, 92 - B. BERENSON: 1932, p. 201 - R. VAN MARLE: vol. XV, 1934, pp. 72-73 - L. SERRA: *L'Arte nelle Marche*, II, Rome, 1934, pp. 247, 251 - B. BERENSON: 1936, p. 173.

PIETRO VANNUCCI CALLED PERUGINO

Castel della Pieva, 1448 c. - Fontignano, 1523

St. John the Evangelist and St. James

Two embroideries in silk with gold and silver thread, 31 × 15 cm. each.

CONDITION: good. PROVENANCE: unknown. Acquired abroad in 1911.

" Of his figures we require no more than that they shall not disturb this feeling, and if we take them as we should, chiefly as architectonic members in the effect of space, they seldom or never disturb us. Their stereotyped attitudes and expressions we should judge, not as if they were persons in a drama, but as so many columns of arches, of which we surely would not demand dramatic variety."

B. BERENSON, *Italian Painters of the Renaissance* - « The Phaidon Press », London, 1952, p. 123.

Very beautiful embroideries based on Perugino designs, datable about 1515. Perhaps they were parts of a cope or a stole.

BIBLIOGRAPHY
Unpublished.

PIETRO VANNUCCI CALLED PERUGINO

Christ in the sarcophagus with landscape in background

Pax with gilded frame. Tempera on panel. 22 × 12 cm.

CONDITION: good. The picture is darkened by dirt. There are some cracks and wormholes in the frame.
PROVENANCE: unknown.

" Perugino... produces his religious effect by means of his space-composition. "
B. BERENSON, Italian Painters of the Renaissance – « The Phaidon Press », London, 1952, p. 123.

This picture, which Berenson attributes to Perugino, develops, in the quietistic spirit of the tiny *Pax*, the iconographic theme already set forth in the small panel of the Louvre, datable about 1473; a theme which will be taken up again, about twenty years later, in the Cyma of the Decennisti Altarpiece, now at the National Gallery, Perugia. Here, linear subtlety, still insistent, melts into the sweet luminous " space " of the beautiful landscape.

BIBLIOGRAPHY
Unpublished.

ANTONIO DA VITERBO CALLED IL PASTURA

Umbria, active from 1478 to 1509

Madonna and Child

Panel, 57 × 41 cm.

CONDITION: damaged during the war; the panel has been cradled. There is some cracking and flaking of pigment. PROVENANCE: unknown.

" The most faithful follower of Pietro Perugino, Antonio da Viterbo ..."

B. BERENSON, Un Botticelli dimenticato, «Dedalo», 1924, V. No. 1.

Typical work of Pinturicchio-like academicism, datable in the first decade of the 16th c.

BIBLIOGRAPHY
B. BERENSON: 1932, p. 31 - B. BERENSON: 1936, p. 27.

LUCA SIGNORELLI

Cortona, 1441-1523

Portraits of Camillo and Vitellozzo Vitelli

Panels, 42 × 33 cm. each. On the upper part of the Vitellozzo portrait are painted the initials: V. V.

CONDITION: fair. PROVENANCE: acquired through Baron Lazzarone in Paris, 1910.

" Luca Signorelli does not glow with Melozzo's consuming fire; and yet he takes his rank beyond. His was the finer and deeper mind, his genius fetched the larger compass, his perception of value, both in life and art, was subtler and more just. Even in feeling for the poetry in things, Luca was inferior to no man. Then—to be more specific—to a sense for tactile values scarcely less than Giotto's, Luca added Masaccio's or Piero della Francesca's command over action. In this indeed, he almost rivalled his own teacher in that art and its unparalleled master, Antonio Pollaiuolo. Great artist he would have been with these qualities alone, but for him they were means to an end, and that end, different from Melozzo's, was his joy in the Nude. "

B. BERENSON, Italian Painters of the Renaissance - « The Phaidon Press », London, 1956, p. 112.

Luca Signorelli was a friend of the Vitellis and these two works must have been part of a series of portraits of members of the family. In fact, the Barber Institute of Fine Arts, Birmingham, Alabama (USA) possesses a Signorelli portrait of Niccolò Vitelli, father of the two brothers pictured in the Berenson collection—Camillo (d. 1496), and Vitellozzo who, after fighting for Charles VIII and Cesare Borgia, was strangled by the latter at Senigallia in 1502. Another son, Paolo, (d. 1499) was a friend of the Medici and commanded the Florentine militia.

The Pinacoteca of Città di Castello contains an entire series of copies of such portraits. Ragghianti Collobi mentions a drawing relating to these portraits on the back of a drawing in the Ecole des Beaux Arts, Paris. Christopher Pudelko has pointed out to me two engravings clearly referring to these paintings in the "Elogium virorum bellica virtute illustrium" of Paolo Giovio (Liber IV—Basel, 1575). Alberto Martini has pointed out that in his "Lives", at the beginning of the Life of Signorelli, Vasari inserted as an authentic likeness of the painter, an engraving derived from the portrait of Vitellozzo Vitelli of the Berenson Collection. The dating of these works varies between about 1492 and 1515. A date toward 1495 would seem plausible.

BIBLIOGRAPHY

L. DUSSLER: *Signorelli*, Berlin, 1927, plates 122, 123 - B. BERENSON: 1932, p. 531 - B. BERENSON: 1936, p. 457 - R. VAN MARLE: vol. XVI, 1937, pp. 51, 100, 116 - L. RAGGHIANTI COLLOBI: *Catalogo della Mostra: Lorenzo il Magnifico e le Arti*, Florence, 1949, p. 54 - M. MORIONDO: *Catalogo della Mostra di Luca Signorelli*, Cortona-Florence, 1953 n. 20, 21 - M. SALMI: *Chiosa Signorelliana* in « Commentari », IV, 1953, p. 112 - M. SALMI: *Luca Signorelli*, Novara, 1953, pp. 18, 53 - A. MARTINI: *Mostra di Luca Signorelli* in « Paragone », IV, 45, 1953, p. 56. - G. COOR: *Neroccio De' Landi*, Princeton, 1961, p. 60 n. 197.

UTILI DA FAENZA

Florentine, active in Faenza from 1476 to 1504, identified as the painter Biagio di Antonio

Ecce Homo

Panel, 46 × 34 cm.

CONDITION: damaged during the war and restored by G. Marchig. PROVENANCE: unknown.

" ... Giovanni Battista Utili of Faenza who was so influenced by Verrocchio and the young Leonardo before he sank to his natural level of a provincial follower of Ghirlandaio."

B. BERENSON, Tre Disegni di Giovan Battista Utili da Faenza in « Rivista d'Arte », XV, 1933, p. 21.

The work bears an attribution to Andrea del Castagno accepted also by Berenson up to the 1936 " Lists" Longhi, however, considers it by a Florentine artist, formerly a follower of Botticellian linearism, after 1470. Later, Berenson proposed the name of Utili da Faenza, that is, Biagio d'Antonio, of Florence.

BIBLIOGRAPHY

R. VAN MARLE, vol. X, 1928, p. 367 - R. LONGHI: *Un Dipinto dell'Angelico a Livorno*, in « Pinacoteca », 1928-29, p. 158 - B. BERENSON: 1932, p. 584 - B. BERENSON: 1936, p. 118.

MICHELE DI MATTEO

Bologna, active first half of XVth century

St. John the Baptist

Panel, 26.2 × 7.5 cm.

CONDITION: good. PROVENANCE: acquired from Mr. Fritz Steinmeyer at Lucerne, 1922.

This work, which Steinmeyer attributed to a Sienese Master of the 14th century, was originally judged by Berenson as a Venetian-Bolognese product of the 15th century. Subsequently, Francesco Arcangeli's correct identification of it as a painting by Michele di Matteo, was accepted by Berenson. Perhaps it decorated a small pilaster of a polyptych.

BIBLIOGRAPHY
Unpublished.

PIETRO ALAMANNO

Göttweih, Austria – Active in the Marches from 1475 to 1497

Madonna and Child amidst garlands of roses and fruits

Panel, 60 × 37 cm. Inscribed on a scroll: *VIRGO ANTE PARTUM—VIRGO POST PARTUM*

CONDITION: good. PROVENANCE: unknown.

" Of ... [Carlo Crivelli's] later style, his well-known pupils and followers, Victor Crivelli and Pietro Alemanno, were the natural heirs; and, as is frequently the case with disciples, they at times anticipated and always outdid their master's exaggerations. Victor, the better workman, was the most prolific, producing flattened and lusterless imitations of his namesake's masterpieces. Intrinsically they are agreeable. Pietro was unequal, and his better moments revealed a painter who was almost an artist."

B. BERENSON, *Venetian Painting in America*, New York, 1916, p. 24.

Berenson originally attributed this work to Matteo da Gualdo, but subsequently ascribed it to Pietro Alamanno. However, the ornamental motives of flowers and fruits, and the character types, aside from their exquisite and subtle linear definition, seem to derive not so much from the manner of Crivelli, but rather from the poetic style of the Ferrarese School about 1470. The influence of Tura is obvious (compare the *Madonna* of the Venice Accademia and the Child of the *Fesch Madonna* of Ajaccio).

BIBLIOGRAPHY
B. BERENSON: 1932, p. 2 - R. VAN MARLE: vol. XV, 1934, p. 85 - B. BERENSON: 1936, p. 2 - B. BERENSON: 1957, vol. I, p. 3.

ERCOLE DE' ROBERTI

Ferrara, c. 1456–1496

St. John the Baptist and St. Jerome

Panels, each 37 × 13 cm.

CONDITION: good. PROVENANCE: Aldo Noseda collection, Milan. EXHIBITIONS: Ferrara Painting of the Renaissance, Ferrara 1933, Nos. 116, 117.

" ... if you stop to think of the substance in the figures represented, you must conclude that they consist of nothing solid, but of some subtle material out of which they were beaten, like repoussé work, having no backs at all, or with hollow insides. "

B. BERENSON, *Italian Painters of the Renaissance* – « The Phaidon Press », London, 1952, p, 103.

Already assigned to Ercole in the Noseda collection, these small pictures are considered, in the Ferrara exhibition catalogue, 1933, as works of the period when the artist was influenced by Venetian painting. Longhi attributes them to the Master whom he had formerly named " Vicino da Ferrara " and whom he subsequently identified as Baldassare d'Este—an opinion accepted by Ortolani, Meiss and Salmi.

BIBLIOGRAPHY

B. BERENSON: *North Italian Painters of the Renaissance*, New York - London, 1907 p. 213 - J. A. CROWE, G. B. CAVALCASELLE: *A History of Painting in North Italy*, (ed. T. Borenius) London, 1912, p. 246 note - B. BERENSON: 1932, p. 484 - CATALOGUE: *Exhibition of Ferrara Painting of the Renaissance*, Ferrara, 1933, p. 99 - R. LONGHI: *Officina Ferrarese*, Rome, 1934 (2nd ed., Florence, 1956, pp. 50, 138) - B. BERENSON: 1936, p. 416 - S. ORTOLANI: *Cosmè Tura, Francesco del Cossa, Ercole de' Roberti*, Milan, 1941, p. 198 - M. MEISS: *Five Ferrarese Panels* in « The Burlington Magazine », March 1951, p. 70 note - M. SALMI: *Ercole de' Roberti*, Milan, 1961, pp. 48, 49.

ERCOLE DE' ROBERTI

Crucifixion

Panel, 31 × 20 cm.

CONDITION: fair. PROVENANCE: bought from Mr. Fritz Steinmeyer in Lucerne, 1922. EXHIBITIONS: Ferrara Painting of the Renaissance, Ferrara 1933. No. 118.

" ... [Ercole's] pattern tends to be calligraphic, as it must be when composed of figures that have more volume than bulk, with limbs at times little more than silhouettes, with feet that seldom press the ground, and hands that never grasp ... But, on the other hand, he had enough feeling for functional line to enable him, if not to communicate movement, to present action so that he succeeded in conveying a sense of things really happening... Moreover, in his best pictures, such as the Dresden *predella*, the figures are so sharply silhouetted, and so frankly treated like repoussé work, that, far from taking them amiss, one is bewitched by their singularity. Finally, his colour has the soothing harmonies of late autumn tints... If miserable decline was the lot of Ercole, who had come in contact with reality at second hand and with intellect at third hand, we may know what to expect from his pupil Lorenzo Costa, whose contact with life and thought was only at third and fourth hand. He began with paintings, like the Bentivoglio portraits and the *Triumphs* in San Giacomo at Bologna, which differ from Ercoli's later works only in increased feebleness of touch and tameness of conception. "

B. BERENSON, *Italian Painters of the Renaissance* - « The Phaidon Press », London, 1952, pp. 163, 164.

Attributed by Berenson, Gamba and Serra to Ercoli de' Roberti, this painting was hesitatingly assigned by Longhi to Lorenzo Costa, as a work of his youthful period when he was influenced by Roberti. Gamba declared that the *Crucifixion* derived from a drawing by Jacopo Bellini (an affirmation repeated by Gronau who even listed the painting among those works " attributed " to Ercole). Longhi, however, has demonstrated the inconsistency of Gamba's derivation. The attribution to Costa is accepted by Salmi, and with some doubts by Ortolani.

BIBLIOGRAPHY

B. BERENSON: 1932, p. 484 - CATALOGUE: *Exhibition of Ferrara Painting of the Renaissance*, Ferrara 1933, p. 100 - C. GAMBA: *Bulletin of the Ferrara Exhibition*, March 1933 - R. LONGHI: *Officina Ferrarese*, Rome, 1934, (2nd Ed., Florence, 1956, pp. 51, 53, 105, 141, 182) - G. GRONAU: *Ercole de' Roberti* in « Thieme-Becker », XXVIII, 1934, p. 426 - B. BERENSON: 1936, p. 416 - W. ARSLAN: Review of: R. LONGHI: *Officina Ferrarese*, in « Zeitschrift », 1936 - S. ORTOLANI: *Cosmè Tura, Francesco del Cossa, Ercole de' Roberti*, Milan, 1941, p. 198 - L. SERRA: *La Mostra della Pittura Ferrarese del Rinascimento*, in « Bollettino d'Arte », 1933, XXVI, p. 582 - B. BERENSON: *Italian Painters of the Renaissance*, London, 1952, plate 343 - M. SALMI: *Ercole de' Roberti*, Milan, 1960, p. 49.

LXIX

ANTONIO DA CREVALCORE

Bologna, documented from 1490–1523

Head of St. Catherine

Panel, 29 × 24 cm. At the bottom, the inscription: *DIVA CATERINA*. On the back of the panel an ancient *graffito* reads: *Cusmè Mŕo di Paneto Mŕo di Benvenuto da Garofalo*.

CONDITION: there is a split on the top of the panel. The colours have oxidized. PROVENANCE: unknown.

Berenson, who had formerly attributed this work, although with hesitation, to Ercole de' Roberti, accepted Zeri's restitution of the painting to Antonio da Crevalcore.

BIBLIOGRAPHY
Unpublished.

LXX

DIVA CATERINA

LEONARDO SCALETTI

Ferrara, mentioned from 1458 to 1495

Angels mourning over decapitated St. Catherine

Panel, 38 × 28 cm.

CONDITION: good. PROVENANCE: unknown.

Although Berenson attributed this small painting to Scaletti, Hendy related it to the work depicting *A Prayer before a Tomb* at the Gardner Museum, Boston, and to the *St. Catherine and a pious woman* at the Carrara Accademia of Bergamo, both products of that Antonio Cicognara whom Longhi distinguished from the older and inferior painter of the Ferrara (formerly Berenson) *Madonna*. The work is datable toward the end of the century.

BIBLIOGRAPHY

P. HENDY: *Antonio Cicognara*, in « Art in America », 1931, p. 48 - B. BERENSON: 1932, p. 516 - B. BERENSON: 1936, p. 443 - E. SANDBERG-VAVALÀ: *Antonio Cicognara again*, in « Art in America », 1937, p. 64 - C. L. RAGGHIANTI: *Review of Sandberg-Vavalà's Article*, in « La Critica d'Arte », XIV, 1938, p. 11.

G. BATTISTA BENVENUTI called ORTOLANO

Ferrara, 1485 c. – died after 1524

Holy Family

Panel, 37 × 30 cm.

CONDITION: panel cradled. The picture is dirty and the colours are in precarious condition. PROVENANCE: unknown.

This delightful and very subtle small painting, which Berenson ascribed to Ortolano, was published by Volpe as a work by Costa, toward 1505. Zeri, however, judges it as the product of Amico Aspertini. The character of the landscape, indeed, seems typical of Aspertini's style in its youthful phase, as does the figure of St. Joseph.

BIBLIOGRAPHY

B. BERENSON: 1932, p. 404 - B. BERENSON: 1936, p. 347 - C. VOLPE: *Alcune Schede per l'Aspertini*, in «Arte Antica e Moderna», 1960, issue 10, p. 168.

JACOPO BELLINI

Venice, 1395–1470

Madonna and Child in benediction

Panel, 64 × 42. Attached to the ledge is a worn cartouche bearing an inscription beginning: *VIRGO DECUS...*

CONDITION: largely repainted. PROVENANCE: unknown.

The painting testifies to the influence which the new Paduan Renaissance ideas exercised on Jacopo between 1440 and 1450. His soft slow-flowing modelling becomes strengthened with shadows, and his forms are arranged in spacious compositions, without, however, entirely subduing the basic Gothic grace of his inspiration.

BIBLIOGRAPHY

B. BERENSON: 1957, I, p. 37.

GIOVANNI BELLINI

Venice, 1427 c. - 1516

Madonna and Child

Transferred from panel to canvas, 75 × 58 cm. The transfer was executed by Genzini, the restoration by G. Marchig. There were many areas missing in the painting which was in very poor condition.

PROVENANCE: unknown.

[With regard to the *Winthrop Madonna*, a variation of this work, Berenson wrote]: " Before a creased curtain, to either side of which appears a bit of landscape [In the *Berenson Madonna*, the landscape only appears on the left side, but the numerous retouchings make it impossible to judge if this represents the original composition], the Blessed Virgin adores the Child, who reclines on a parapet. She is a monumental figure, grandly draped, one of Bellini's noblest types of womanhood. Few of his Madonnas have more amplitude of design; or a more convincing existence."

B. BERENSON, *Venetian Painting in America* - New York, 1916, p. 78.

Judged by Berenson as a youthful work, this *Madonna*, which might be dated about 1479, is composed according to a scheme developed in various ways by the Master from the time of the *Davis Madonna*. We find it in the *Madonna* of the Contini Bonacossi collection in Florence, in the Madonna (No. 2901), of the National Gallery, London, and in the Madonna of the Verona Museum (No. 110). The *Winthrop Madonna* of the Fogg Art Museum, Cambridge, which Berenson published as a studio product, and related to the present work of his own possession, repeats the same composition in reverse.

BIBLIOGRAPHY

B. BERENSON: *Venetian Painting in America*, New York, 1916, p. 80 note - B. BERENSON: 1932, p. 70 - B. BERENSON: 1936, p. 61 - C. GAMBA: *Giovanni Bellini*, Milan, 1937, plate 100 - M. DAVIES: *The Earlier Italian School - National Gallery Catalogues*, London 1951, p. 55 - B. BERENSON: 1957, vol. I, p. 30 - S. BOTTARI: *Giovanni Bellini*, in « Enciclopedia Universale dell'Arte », 1958, vol. II, p. 52 - R. PALLUCCHINI: *Giovanni Bellini*, Milan, 1959, p. 139.

Pietà

Panel, 59 × 48 cm.

CONDITION: missing areas. Restored by A. Vermehren. PROVENANCE: acquired in 1916 from A. Briganti.

" ... that great but unconscious revolutionary, Giovanni Bellini, hitherto an adept of the plastic vision, began all at once to visualize in still another mode, which, to differentiate it from the linear and the plastic, I may call the commencement of the pictorial mode. This happened because he had a revelation of the possibilities of colour. Before his day, except in a rudimentary way at Verona, colour, no matter how enchanting in its beauty, was a mere ornament added to the real materials, which were line in the fourteenth century, and line filled with light and shade in the fifteenth. With Bellini colour began to be the material of the painter, the chief if not the sole instrument with which his effects were to be produced. Yet Bellini never dreamt of abandoning the shapes which the plastic vision had evolved; he simply rendered them henceforth with colour instead of with line and chiaroscuro; he merely gave up the plastic-linear for the plastic-pictorial."

B. BERENSON, *Italian Painters of the Renaissance* – « The Phaidon Press », London, 1952, p. 172.

Acquired as a work of the school of Bellini, Berenson attributed this Pietà to the Master, an attribution accepted by Gamba and rejected by Dussler. As far as it may be judged in view of the poor condition of the work, the nobility and tragic severity of the composition and exceptional beauty of the landscape, are not unworthy of Bellini himself, toward 1480.

BIBLIOGRAPHY

B. BERENSON: 1932, p. 70 - B. BERENSON: 1936, p. 61: C. GAMBA: *Giovanni Bellini*, Milan, 1937, pp. 87-88 - L. DUSSLER: *Giovanni Bellini*, Vienna, 1949, p. 65 - B. BERENSON: 1957, vol. I, p. 30.

GIAN BATTISTA CIMA DA CONEGLIANO

Conegliano, 1460 c. – 1518 c.

St. Sebastian

Panel, 100 × 49 cm.

CONDITION: the painting was cleaned and restored years ago, but the pigment is again in poor condition.
PROVENANCE: unknown.

" After Giovanni Bellini and Carpaccio and before Giorgione, the best beloved painter of Venice remains Cima da Conegliano. No wonder, for no other master of that time paints so well the pearly hazes that model the Italian landscape with a peculiar lightness and breadth. He calls up memories of hours spent among the foothills of Alps and Apennines, cool and covered with violet grey mist. His castles, his streams and his foliage have the same gift of recalling and even communicating pleasant states of body and mind. His figures are severe and chaste but seldom morose, and occasionally they have quivering nostrils and mouths of surprising sensitiveness. I seem to recognize in his women a kinship to certain of ours, produced by generations of puritanic repression and selection and rebellion."

" So much for Cima's character as an illustrator. Judged by the requirements of decoration, he stands only under Bellini. He is a draughtsman of strenuous and exquisite precision, with a sense of line scarcely surpassed in Venice. His colouring is transparent, cool, pearly, and nevertheless seldom if ever cold or harsh. His modelling is firm, at times rather suggesting porcelain. Yet he has neither the abandon of a Carpaccio nor the intimacy of a Giovanni Bellini. He remains more external, more schematic, as if he constructed rather than created his figures; and in this, as in certain other respects, resembles Mantegna."

B. BERENSON, *Venetian Painting in America*, New York, 1916, pp. 186-187.

Masterpiece by Cima; might be dated about 1500. The composition repeats the St. Sebastian of the *Holy Conversation*, No. 36 (Dragan Altarpiece) of the Venice Accademia, but the figure, isolated as it is in the landscape, assumes a far more poetic and solemn serenity and grandeur. The work should be compared with the similar subject, equally beautiful, at the Strassbourg Museum.

BIBLIOGRAPHY

G. FRIZZONI: *La Raccolta Mond ed Opere Attinenti alla Medesima*, in « Rassegna d'Arte », XI, 1911, pp. 25-31, 43-48 - J. A. CROWE, G. B. CAVALCA-SELLE: *A History of Painting in North Italy*, (ed. T. Borenius), London 1912, I, p. 252 note - D. VON HADELN: in « Thieme-Becker », VI, 1912, p. 595 - B. BERENSON: 1932, p. 146 - B. BERENSON: 1936, p. 126 - R. VAN MARLE: vol. XVII, 1935, p. 433 - R. LONGHI: *Viatico per Cinque Secoli di Pittura Veneziana*, Florence, 1946, p. 60 - B. BERENSON: 1957, I, p. 65 - L. COLETTI: *Cima*, Venice, 1959, p. 79 n. 43.

GIAN BATTISTA CIMA DA CONEGLIANO

Story of Coriolanus (?)

Panels of a cassone 37 × 89 cm., each.

CONDITION: fair. PROVENANCE: purchased from Luigi Grassi.

" In general, Cima tends to get more atmospheric as he advances, to envelope his figures more, to be more detailed in his landscape and to get more coloured."

B. BERENSON, *Venetian Painting in America*, New York, 1916, p. 188.

These frontal sections of a cassone should be related also to that of the Schraffl (formerly Bölher) collection of Zurich, exhibited in London at the great 1930 show with No. 274, and another one, mentioned by Ragghianti (c. f. Introduction to O. Kurz, *Falsi e falsari*, Venice, 1961, p. XVIII) repainted at the left with the addition of a dragon, so as to transform the Roman story into a depiction of St. George. Coletti (1959) who dates this work around 1500, discerns a Giorgionesque spirit in it, as in the *Judith* of the Rasini collection of Milan, prompting him to propose the name of the youthful Giorgione.

BIBLIOGRAPHY

B. BERENSON: 1932, p. 146 - B. BERENSON: 1936, p. 126 - R. VAN MARLE: vol. XVII, 1935, p. 455 note I - B. BERENSON: 1957, I, p. 65 - L. COLETTI: *Cima*, Venice, 1959, pp. 55, 81.

DOMENICO MORONE

Verona, born about 1442 – died after 1517

Prisoner before Judge

Tondo on panel, 32 cm. in diameter.

CONDITION: good, colour dirty. PROVENANCE: unknown.

" The tendency... manifested most clearly and potently in Domenico Morone, was to admit nothing of the old spirit in adopting the new imagery and the new attitudes introduced by Mantegna... But Mantegna's influence upon Morone ran contrary to intimacy with reality, and swept him away towards schematization and towards that kind of elegance which, in happy circumstances, is the first as well as the finest product of this kind of intensification."

B. BERENSON, Italian Painters of the Renaissance – « The Phaidon Press », London, 1952, pp. 167, 168.

Cassone decoration, typical of the art of Verona. Dated about 1495.

BIBLIOGRAPHY

P. SCHUBRING: *Cassoni-Supplement*, Leipzig, 1923, p. 6 n. 955 - B. BERENSON: 1932, p. 376 - B. BERENSON: 1936, p. 323 - R. BRENZONI: *Domenico Morone*, Florence, 1956, p. 41.

FRANCESCO BONSIGNORI

Verona, 1455? – 1519?

Apollo and Daphne

Panel, 38 × 48 cm.

CONDITION: Damaged during the war and restored by G. Marchig. Panel cradled. The colours are faded, and there is some overpainting. PROVENANCE: unknown.

" Although a Veronese by birth, and first trained, no doubt, by a Mantegnesque compatriot, and later in life himself sucked into the current of Mantegna, he was for some years in his early manhood so strongly influenced by the Vivarini and Giovanni Bellini as to count among the Venetians. His paintings of those years betray, too, as is natural, a certain acquaintance with Antonello, but far less than we shall find in the works of Montagna or Cima."

B. BERENSON, *Venetian Painting in America*, New York, 1916, p. 170.

Probably a decorative panel of a cassone, which might be dated in the last decade of the 15th century.

BIBLIOGRAPHY

B. BERENSON: 1932, p. 96 - B. BERENSON: 1936, p. 83.

MARCO DI GIORGIO BELLO

Venice, 1470-1523

Holy Family with St. John and Bishop Saint

Panel, 37 × 52 cm.

CONDITION: fair. The panel has been cradled. PROVENANCE: unknown.

The Virgin of this painting is almost identical with that of the *Madonna and Child*, No. 318, of the Carrara Academy of Bergamo, for which the painter employed the same " cartoon ", with slight differences, as he also did for the *Madonna and Child with Infant St. John*, No. 101, of the Academy of Venice, of which several versions exist (cf. Catalogue of the Gallery of the Venice Academy, 1955, I, p. 111, No. 111), all tracing back to the pattern set by Vincenzo Catena. The work may be dated about 1520.

BIBLIOGRAPHY

B. BERENSON: 1957, I, p. 39.

LXXX

G. FRANCESCO DAL ZOTTO DA TOLMEZZO

Tolmezzo, c. 1450–1510

Epiphany

Panel, 7 × 37.

CONDITION: poor, unclean, pigment flaking. PROVENANCE: unknown.

This wooden and naïve provincial transcription in the manner of the Paduan and Murano schools is a typical example of the Friullian painter's work.

BIBLIOGRAPHY
B. BERENSON: 1957, I, p. 83.

VINCENZO FOPPA

Brescia 1427 c. – 1516 c.

Madonna and Child with Angel Musicians (Madonna of the Hedge)

Panel, 42 × 42 cm.

CONDITION: panel cradled and painting restored. PROVENANCE: A. Noseda collection, Milan. EXHIBITIONS: Lombard Art from the Visconti to the Sforza, Milan, 1958, No. 296.

" Quattrocento painting in Milan, as we know it at least, owed its existence to Vincenzo Foppa. Although in composition and landscape he occasionally shows traces of Pisanellesque training, he got his serious education at Padua along with Bellini, Mantegna, and Tura. His achievement, as represented by works that have come down to us, is less in quantity and probably also in quality than that of his fellows. Yet it may be questioned whether, putting Mantegna on one side, Foppa's native talents were inferior to Tura's or even to the Bellinis."

B. BERENSON, Italian Painters of the Rénaissance - « The Phaidon Press », London, 1952, pp. 176-177.

The left side of the painting—with the *Violinist Angel*—belonged to the Aldo Noseda collection and was joined to the rest, which was in Milan in the Trivulzio collection, by the restorer Cavenaghi, who replaced the trees in the background. Previously, the Trivulzio fragment was at Cremona, where it was acquired by the antiquarian Cantoni and attributed to Foppa by G. Bertini. The reassembled work passed into the Noseda collection and thence to Bernard Berenson.

The work is unanimously deemed as belonging to the Master's youthful period, between 1445 and 1450, prior to his stay at Padua. The interpretation of Lombard and Veronese stylistic and iconographic motifs, courtly-gothic in expression, already reveal the poetic naturalism that will be characteristic of the artist's maturity.

BIBLIOGRAPHY

Catalogo della Collezione del fu Conte Luciano Passalacqua, part II, Milan, 1887 (the fragment with the *Violinist Angel*, attributed to V. Civerchio, is listed as No. 22) - G. FRIZZONI: *Rassegna di Insigni Artisti Italiani: Vincenzo Foppa*, in « L'Arte », II, 1899, p. 322 - B. BERENSON: *North Italian Painters of the Renaissance*, London, 1907, p. 219 - J. C. FFOULKES, R. MAJOCCHI: *Vincenzo Foppa of Brescia*, London, 1909, pp. 8 ff. - W. SUIDA: *Studien zur Lombardischen Malerei des XV. Jhd.* Leipzig, 1909, p. 479 - P. TOESCA: *La pittura e la Miniatura nella Lombardia dai più Antichi Monumenti alla Metà del Quattrocento*, Milan, 1912, pp. 576-7 - A. VENTURI: VII, p. IV, 1915, pp. 838-40, plate 550 - F. WITTGENS: *Vincenzo Foppa*, Milan, 1948, pp. 14, 91 - B. BERENSON: 1932, p. 199 - B. BERENSON: 1936, p. 171 - C. BARONI, S. SAMEK LUDOVICI: *La Pittura Lombarda del Quattrocento*, Messina-Florence, 1952, p. 127 - F. WITTGENS: *La Pittura Lombarda nella Seconda Metà del Quattrocento*, in « Storia di Milano », Fondazione Treccani, Milan, 1956, part. VII, p. 750 - F. MAZZINI: in *Catalogo della Mostra d'Arte Lombarda dai Visconti agli Sforza*, Milan, 1958, pp. 97-98.

VINCENZO FOPPA

Madonna nursing the Child

Panel, 49 × 36 cm.

CONDITION: restored. PROVENANCE: formerly in the Crespi collection, Milan (No. 26 in Catalogue of the Crespi sale), was acquired by B. Berenson in 1916 at Paris from Trotti & Co. EXHIBITIONS: Exhibition of Brescian painting of the Renaissance, Brescia, 1939 No. 20.

This *Madonna*, among Foppa's most beautiful works, has been correctly dated by Wittgens between 1460 and 1470. Wittgens considers it close to the frescoes of the Portinari Chapel in St. Eustorgio of Milan.

BIBLIOGRAPHY

J. A. CROWE, G. B. CAVALCASELLE: *A History of Painting in North Italy*, (ed. by T. Borenius), London, 1912, vol. II, p. 327 - B. BERENSON: *The North Italian Painters of the Renaissance*, London, 1907, p. 219 - C. J. FFOULKES e R. MAJOCCHI: *Vincenzo Foppa of Brescia*, London, 1909, p. 86 - A. VENTURI: vol. VII, part IV, 1915, pp. 844-846 - A. VENTURI: *La Pittura del Quattrocento nell'Alta Italia*, Bologna, 1930, p. 17 - B. BERENSON: 1932, p. 199 - B. BERENSON: 1936, p. 171 - A. MORASSI: *Vincenzo Foppa*, in « Enciclopedia Italiana Treccani », XV, p. 653 - R. LONGHI: *Quesiti Caravaggeschi*, in « Pinacoteca », 1929, n. 5-6, p. 264 - F. LECHI, G. PANAZZA: *Catalogo della Mostra della Pittura Bresciana del Rinascimento*, Brescia 1939, p. 57 n. 20 - F. WITTGENS: *Vincenzo Foppa*, Milan, 1948, pp. 39, 96 - C. BARONI, S. SAMEK LUDOVICI: *La Pittura Lombarda del Rinascimento*, Messina-Florence, 1952, p. 158 - B. BERENSON: *Italian Painters of the Renaissance*, London, 1952, plate 361 - F. WITTGENS: *La Pittura Lombarda nella Seconda Metà del Quattrocento*, in « Storia di Milano », Fondazione Treccani, Milan, 1956, part VII, p. 758.

VINCENZO FOPPA

Martyrdom of St. Sebastian

Panel, 32.5 × 26 cm.

CONDITION: the panel is cradled. Traces of old restorations are evident in the unclean sections of the painting. PROVENANCE: from the De Cristoforis collection the work passed to the Grandi Brothers, from whom B. Berenson acquired it after 1916. EXHIBITIONS: Brescian Renaissance painting, Brescia 1939. (No. 5).

" As perhaps no other master of his time, he tends to soften the impact between surface and atmosphere, and his feeling for colour is in accord, for he prefers silvery, almost shimmering effects, bordering on monochrome."

B. BERENSON, *Italian Painters of the Renaissance* – « The Phaidon Press », London, p. 177.

A work of Foppa's maturity, about 1470. Considered by Baroni as contemporaneous with the painting of a similar subject in the Museum of the Castello di Milano; Testori, however, places it earlier than that work or the one in the Brera by several years.

BIBLIOGRAPHY

M. CAFFI: *Vincenzo Civerchio* in « Archivio Storico Italiano », 1883, p. 342 - C. J. FFOULKES, R. MAJOCCHI: *Vincenzo Foppa of Brescia*, London, 1909, p. 144 - G. FRIZZONI: *Vincenzo Foppa Pittore*, in « L'Arte », VII, 1909, p. 254 - F. MALAGUZZI VALERI: *Il Foppa in una Recente Pubblicazione*, in « Rassegna d'Arte », 1909, p. 86 - W. SUIDA: *Studien zur Lombardischen Malerei des XV. Jhd.*, Leipzig, 1909, p. 480 - G. PAULI: *Vincenzo Foppa*, in «Thieme-Becker», XII, (1916), p. 196 - R. LONGHI: *Quesiti Caravaggeschi*, in « Pinacoteca », 1929, n. 5-6, p. 264 - A. VENTURI: *La Pittura del Quattrocento nell'Alta Italia*, Bologna, 1930, p. 18 - B. BERENSON: 1932, p. 199 - B. BERENSON: 1936, p. 171 - P. LECHI, G. PANAZZA: *Catalogo della Mostra della Pittura Bresciana del Rinascimento*, Brescia, 1939, p. 35, n. 5 - F. WITTGENS: *Vincenzo Foppa*, Milan, 1948, pp. 68, 101 - C. BARONI, S. SAMEK LUDOVICI: *La Pittura Lombarda del Quattrocento*, Messina-Florence, 1952, p. 164 - G. TESTORI: *Un S. Sebastiano del Foppa*, in « Paragone » 87, March, 1957, p. 58.

AMBROGIO DA FOSSANO CALLED BERGOGNONE

Milan (?), 1470 c. – 1522

Madonna and Angels in Adoration of the Child

Panel, 70 × 53 cm.

CONDITION: damaged during the war. Restored by G. Marchig. The panel is cracked, the pigment dirty. PROVENANCE: unknown.

" The most remarkable of Foppa's followers was Ambrogio Bergognone—one is tempted to say the most remarkable native painter of the whole Milanese land. It is true that his range is limited, seldom carrying him beyond the horizon of his master, and it is also true that he is not conspicuous for peculiar excellence in form or movement or space-composition. Nor is he altogether free from the feebleness of the imitator, and from the prettiness which, in his later years, was deluging his country. But he has left us one of the most restrained, most profound, and most refined expressions in art of genuine piety. Were Christian piety the real source of the pleasure that religious people take in painting, they would greatly prefer Bergognone to their actual favourites, Fra Angelico, or Francia, or Perugino. But they are attracted consciously by the sweetness of type in all these masters, and unconsciously by the charm of line and colour in Angelico, the cool green meadows of Francia, and the space harmonies of Perugino. The Milanese is not so appealing on any of these grounds; nevertheless, besides being a rare and noble illustrator, he was all but a great painter. "

B. BERENSON, *Italian Painters of the Renaissance* - « The Phaidon Press », London, 1952, p. 178.

This masterpiece by Bergognone, which Berenson and Cagnola considered a youthful work, perhaps goes back to the earliest period of his activity for the Certosa of Pavia, toward 1488.

BIBLIOGRAPHY

G. CAGNOLA: *Intorno al Bergognone*, in « Rassegna d'Arte », 1914, p. 220 - B. BERENSON: 1932, p. 98 - B. BERENSON: 1936, p. 84 - I. M. SACCO: *Il Bergognone*, Fossano, 1938, p. 98 - N. APRÀ: *Ambrogio da Fossano detto il Bergognone*, Milan, 1945, p. 10 - F. MAZZINI: *Ambrogio Bergognone*, Brescia, 1948.

AMBROGIO DA FOSSANO CALLED BERGOGNONE

Madonna and Child.
In background: *Flight into Egypt and Massacre of the Innocents*

Panel, 45 × 38 cm.

CONDITION: good. PROVENANCE: gift of Count Alessandro Contini Bonacossi.

" As a painter, he came perhaps as near as possible for a man firmly fixed in habits of plastic visualizing to being a Renaissance Whistler. He had Whistler's passion for harmonies of tone, and synthetized, abbreviated, symbolized drawing. Such drawing could scarcely assert itself against the plastic sturdiness of his figures in altar-pieces, nor yet (although somewhat more) when he was putting in a set landscape; but in the glimpses he gives of city streets, of stretches of canal, of rural bits, and at times in quite small figures, his taste was more free to follow its bent. He then reminds one, as no other Italian, of the exquisite American."

B. BERENSON, *Italian Painters of the Renaissance* - « The Phaidon Press », London, 1952, pp. 178-179.

A work of excellent quality, datable somewhat after 1490.

BIBLIOGRAPHY
Unpublished.

LORENZO LOTTO

Venice, c. 1480 - Loreto, 1556

Christ on the Cross and the Symbols of the Passion

Panel, 18 × 14.3 cm. Written on the back: " *Questo quadro è fatto di mano di Messer Lorenzo Lotto, omo molto divoto, et per sua divotione il fece la septimana santa et fu finito il Venerdì-Santo all'ora della Passione di N. S. Gesù Cristo. Io Zanetto del Co. ho scritto acciò si sappia e sia tenuta in quella venerazione che merita essa figura.*"
[" *This painting is by the hand of Messer Lorenzo Lotto, a very devout man, and he made it out of his devotion during Holy Week, and it was finished on Good Friday at the hour of the Passion of our Lord Jesus Christ. I, Zanetto del Co. have written so that it be known and held in that veneration which this picture deserves.*"]
Perhaps the writing is by the architect, Zuan del Coro, of Ancona.

CONDITION: good. PROVENANCE: from the Borromeo collection, Milan. Gift of Count Alessandro Contini Bonacossi.

" ... we must give a glance to a little picture which betrays, in contrast to the modern feeling that we shall find in the Cingoli altarpiece, an almost mediaeval view of Christianity, as if to remind us, this time, that in Lotto, as in so many of his contemporaries, the old and the new could lie peacefully in separate strata of a man's nature, unconscious as yet of their reciprocal antagonism... Christ hangs on the Cross with the various scenes of the Passion indicated in a kind of pictorial shorthand as in a number of Trecento and early Quattrocento pictures, ... The modelling and the effects of light bring this little panel close to the Ancona altarpiece ... but I place it considerably earlier because it usually happens that the signs of an advanced style appear sooner in pictures with small figures than in important works of larger size, and also because in type and action the Christ is scarcely changed from the one at Monte San Giusto. Indeed, in some respects, the panel stands closer to the St. Lucy predella of 1532 than to any other works."

B. BERENSON, *Lorenzo Lotto* - « The Phaidon Press », London, 1956, pp. 88-89.

BIBLIOGRAPHY

B. BERENSON: *Lorenzo Lotto - An essay in Constructive Art Criticism*, New-York, London, 1895, Reprinted *Lorenzo Lotto* (The Phaidon Press, London, 1956) - G. FRIZZONI: *Lorenzo Lotto Pittore. A Proposito di una Nuova Pubblicazione* in « Archivio Storico dell'Arte », 1896, p. 429 - B. BERENSON: 1932, p. 309 - B. BERENSON: 1936, p. 266 - A. BANTI, A. BOSCHETTO: *Lorenzo Lotto*, Florence, s.d., p. 85 - P. BIANCONI: *Tutta la Pittura di Lorenzo Lotto*, Milan, 1955, p. 62 - B. BERENSON: 1957, p. 102.

VENETIAN MASTER
ABOUT 1530

Madonna and Child, St. Francis and St. Joseph

Panel, 74 × 54 cm.

CONDITION: good. PROVENANCE: unknown.

" Very close to Lotto, so close indeed that I am perhaps hypercritical in refusing to assign it to him, is the *Holy Family with St. Francis* in my own collection. The Madonna holds the Child uneasily on her drawn-up right knee. The fine Titianesque head of St. Francis in profile against the sky to our left and a bearded St. Joseph to right in the shadow of a green curtain. The general intonation silvery. Whoever painted this panel must have done it about 1530."

B. BERENSON, Lorenzo Lotto – « The Phaidon Press », London, 1956, p. 140.

Berenson always hesitated to attribute this fine painting to Lorenzo Lotto, although that Master would seem to be the one whose quality and style most closely approximate those found in this work. The painting, very similar in manner to Antonio Palma (Zeri), is certainly by the hand of the same Bergamesque artist who produced the *Madonna and Saints* in the Parochial Church of Clusone as Professor Pellicioli has indicated. (cf. A. Venturi, " Storia dell'Arte ", vol. IX, part VII, fig. 114).

BIBLIOGRAPHY

B. BERENSON: 1932, p. 308 - B. BERENSON: 1936, p. 265 - L. COLETTI: *Lorenzo Lotto*, Bergamo, 1953 - B. BERENSON: *Lotto*, 1955, p. 181 - P. BIANCONI: *Tutta la Pittura di Lorenzo Lotto*, Milan, 1955, p. 75 - B. BERENSON: 1957, I, p. 102.

BONIFAZIO VERONESE DE' PITATI

Venice, 1487-1553

Pompey's head brought to Caesar

Panel, 25 × 51 cm.

CONDITION: good. PROVENANCE: unknown.

" ... [Palma's] pupil, Bonifazio... under such titles as *The Rich Man's Feast* or *The Finding of Moses*, painting all the scenes of fashionable country life, music on the terrace of a villa, hunting parties, and picnics in the forest."

B. BERENSON, *Italian Painters of the Renaissance* - « The Phaidon Press », London, 1952, p. 30.

In this painting, elegant manneristic figures move harmoniously in the atmospheric vastness of the landscape. The work should be considered in connection with the *Muzio Scevola e Porsenna* of the Mrs. Julius Weitzner collection, New York.

BIBLIOGRAPHY

D. WESTPHAL: *Bonifazio Veronese*, Munich, 1931 - B. BERENSON: 1957, p. 42.

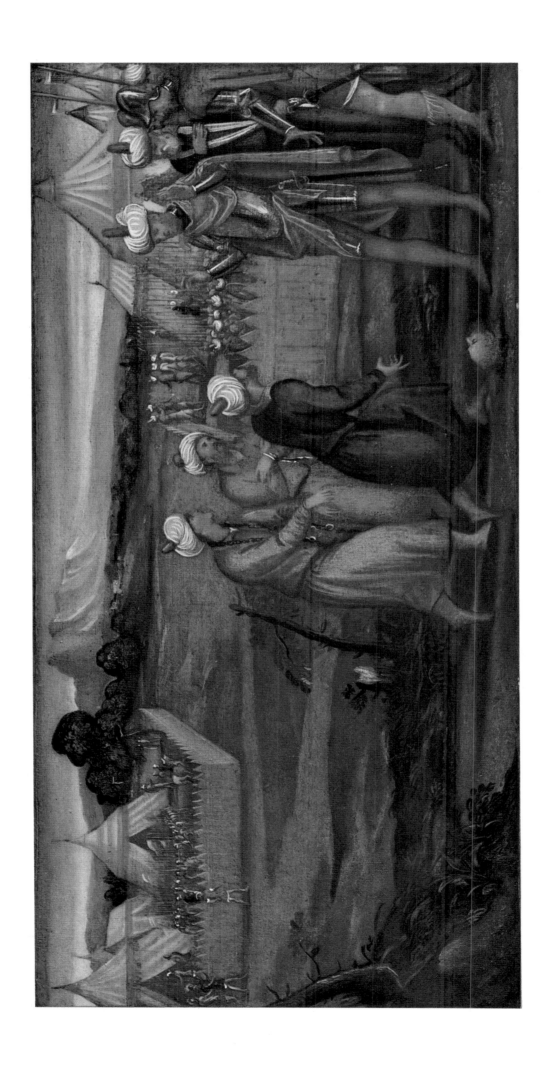

NICCOLÒ GIOLFINO

Verona, c. 1477-1555

Story of Phaeton

Two cassone panels—Panels, 14 × 25 cm. each.

CONDITION: poor. The painting has deteriorated considerably. PROVENANCE: unknown.

" We need not linger here over such followers of Liberale as Giolfino, with his taste for ugliness occasionally relieved by a certain whimsical winsomeness ..."

B. BERENSON, Italian Painters of the Renaissance – « The Phaidon Press », London, 1952, p. 171.

Among the finest works of Giolfino, revealing to the highest degree his sensitivity to atmosphere, and his graceful classicism.

BIBLIOGRAPHY

B. BERENSON: *The North Italian Painters of the Renaissance*, New York-London, 1900, p. 236 - P. SCHUBRING: *Cassoni*, Leipzig, 1915, p. 379, Nos. 703, 704 - B. BERENSON: 1932, p. 231 - B. BERENSON: 1936, p. 199.

PARIS BORDONE

Treviso, 1500 – Venice, 1571

Rest on the flight to Egypt and the legend of St. Hubert

Panel, 34 × 88 cm.

CONDITION: damaged during the war and restored by G. Marchig. PROVENANCE: acquired in London from Dowdeswell and Dowdeswell, 1910.

" ... the painter remains festive, sensual, and fleshly."

B. BERENSON, *Catalogue of Italian Paintings*, M. G. Johnson, Philadelphia, 1913, vol. I. p. 129.

Work completely in the spirit of the richest and most mellow Titianesque use of colour.

BIBLIOGRAPHY

B. BERENSON: 1932, p. 430 - B. BERENSON: 1936, p. 370 - B. BERENSON: 1957, I, p. 46.

SEBASTIANO LUCIANI called DEL PIOMBO

Venice, c. 1485-1547

Portrait of a Gentleman

Canvas, 59 × 45 cm.

CONDITION: fair, the painting has lost some of its tonality. PROVENANCE: unknown.

" The one Venetian who became an eclectic remained in spite of it a great painter. Sebastiano del Piombo fell under the influence of Michelangelo, but while this influence was pernicious in most cases, the hand that had learned to paint under Bellini, Cima, and Giorgione never wholly lost its command of colour and tone."

B. BERENSON, Italian Painters of the Renaissance – « The Phaidon Press », London, 1952, p. 24.

Considered by Berenson as one of Sebastiano's late works, this weak portrait is perhaps an old copy of a Titianesque prototype. The attribution was doubted by Gombosi and Pallucchini and has, in fact, been decisively rejected by Dussler.

BIBLIOGRAPHY

G. BERNARDINI: *Sebastiano del Piombo*, Bergamo 1908, p. 62 - A. VENTURI: vol. IX, part 5, p. 81 - G. GOMBOSI: *Piombo fra' Sebastiano* in « Thieme-Becker », XXXVI, 1933 - B. BERENSON: 1932, p. 521 - B. BERENSON: 1936, p. 448 - L. DUSSLER: *Sebastiano del Piombo*, Basel, 1942, p. 157 - P. PALLUCCHINI: *Sebastian Viniziano*, Milan, 1944, p. 188 - B. BERENSON: 1957 I, p. 168.

ANDREA DEL BRESCIANINO

Active at Siena from 1507 to after 1525

St. Catherine of Alexandria

Panel, 59 × 42 cm.

CONDITION: good. The restoration revealed the attributes of the St. Catherine, previously covered by an overpainting, so that the work seemed to be a *Portrait of a Woman*. Indeed, that is how it is referred to by Misciattelli, Venturi, and even Berenson in the "Lists" of 1932. PROVENANCE: unknown.

"He was a pretty, winning painter who, at his best, fused, very charmingly, certain merely attractive elements in the styles of Fra Bartolommeo, Andrea del Sarto and Raphael, with his native Sienese qualities. Despite eclecticism, he, like most eclectics, is very easy to recognize. He generally gives a high forehead, eyelids almost without modelling under eyebrows that stretch way beyond them, rather full tipped noses and small mouths. The hands tend to be ovular with the fingers like straight sticks. The draperies are apt to consist of long or angular folds. The drawing is timid, the modelling vague and almost structural. I frequently think of Brescianino as a very unsubstantial ghost of Raphael who sometimes coalesces with equally attenuated spectres of Fra Bartolommeo and Andrea del Sarto."

B. BERENSON, From the author's original manuscript of: *Le Portrait Raphaëlesque de Montpellier*, « Gazette des Beaux-Arts », 1907, I, pp. 210-212.

BIBLIOGRAPHY

B. BERENSON: *The Central Italian Painters of the Renaissance*, London - New York, 1909, p. 155 - J. A. CROWE, G. B. CAVALCASELLE: *A History of Painting in North Italy*, (T. Borenius ed.), London, 1914, VI, p. 27, n. 2 - P. MISCIATTELLI: *La Donna Senese del Rinascimento*, in « La Diana », 1927, II, p. 258 note - A. VENTURI: vol. IX, p. V, 1932, p. 372 note - B. BERENSON: 1932, p. 112 - B. BERENSON: 1936, p. 97.

FRANCESCO UBERTINI called BACHIACCA

Florence, 1495–1557

Leda

Panel, 25 × 20 cm.

CONDITION: good. PROVENANCE: unknown.

" The Florentine followers of Raphael fall quickly to the low level of a Bachiacca, who never knows how to assimilate his thefts, but makes a parade of them, like a Fiji islander, strutting about in cast-off European garments."

B. BERENSON, *The Study and Criticism of Italian Art*, London, 1902, II, p. 40.

Youthful masterpiece, datable prior to 1520, a bit before the *Leda* of the J. Linsky collection, New York.

BIBLIOGRAPHY

A. MC COMB: *Francesco Ubertini (Bachiacca)*, in « The Art Bulletin », vol. VIII, n. 3, 1926, pp. 140-167 - B. BERENSON: 1932, p. 35 - B. BERENSON: 1936, p. 30 - R. SALVINI: *Ubertini*, in « Thieme-Becker », XXXIII, 1939, p. 522 - L. MARCUCCI: *Contributo al Bachiacca*, in « Bollettino d'Arte », 1958, p. 34.

SCHOOL OF VERCELLI
XVITH CENTURY (?)

Old man in a room (Allegory of waiting for death)

Panel, 50 × 40 cm.

CONDITION: fair: the pigment is darkened by dirt and varnish. PROVENANCE: unknown.

Berenson cautiously attributes this to the school of Vercelli. However, certain stylistic and iconographic characteristics of this rare painting bring a general Flemish environment to mind, without fixing upon a specific painter. The architectural elements are Italianate, but undoubtedly of Flemish structure and taste: for example, details of furnishing and dress. Observe, also, the painting represented on the walls of the room, with the *Final Judgment* recalling Nordic works. Perhaps the painting was derived from an engraving.

BIBLIOGRAPHY
Unpublished.

Hercules and Antaeus, and other labours of Hercules

Panel, 143 × 98 cm.

Condition: poor, with cracks and flaking of pigment. Provenance: unknown.

Assigned by Berenson to the Dutch School, this panel is the work of a " Romanist " Master in the circle of Hans Baldung Grien; it suffices to compare it with paintings of a similar subject in the Museums of Cassel, Breslau, etc., of which this is a variation.

BIBLIOGRAPHY
Unpublished.

JEAN MARC NATTIER

Paris, 1685-1766

Portrait of the Duchess of Orléans

Canvas, 46 × 38 cm.

CONDITION: good. PROVENANCE: acquired from C. Brunner in Paris, 1909. EXHIBITIONS: " La Peinture française à Florence ", Florence 1945.

" The fresh and gay Nattier with his allegorized portraits of the royal princesses and other great ladies..."

B. BERENSON, *From the author's original manuscript for the Introduction to the Catalogue of the Exhibition*: « Le peinture Française à Florence, » Florence, 1945, p. 12.

This is a sketch for the portrait in the Stockholm Museum, dated 1744.

BIBLIOGRAPHY

P. DE NOLHAC: *Nattier*, Paris, 1905, Catalogue of the Exhibition: *La Peinture Française à Florence*, Florence, 1945, p. 446, n. 52.

PIETRO LONGHI

Venice, 1702-1785

The card game

Canvas, 68 × 52 cm.

CONDITION: the colour is dirty. PROVENANCE: acquired in London, 1900 from J. P. Richter. The painting came from the Cavendish-Bentinck collection.

" The love for pictures was by no means dead in Venice, and Longhi painted for the picture-loving Venetians their own lives in all their ordinary domestic and fashionable phases. In the hairdressing scenes we hear the gossip of the periwigged barber; in the dressmaking scenes, the chatter of the maid; in the dancing school, the pleasant music of the violin. There is no tragic note anywhere. Everybody dresses, dances, makes bows, takes coffee, as if there was nothing else in the world that wanted doing. A tone of high courtesy, of great refinement, coupled with an all-pervading cheerfulness, distinguishes Longhi's pictures from the works of Hogarth, at once so brutal and so full of presage of change."

B. BERENSON, *Italian Painters of the Renaissance* - « The Phaidon Press », 1952, pp. 33-34.

Although the work has always borne a Longhi attribution, the work is an imitation of the Master's style by a contemporary.

BIBLIOGRAPHY
Unpublished.

FRANCESCO ZUCCARELLI

Pitigliano, 1702 – Florence, 1788

Two landscapes with figures

Oil on canvas, 42 × 46 cm. each.

CONDITION: good. PROVENANCE: unknown.

Decorative paintings in the manner of Francesco Zuccarelli.

BIBLIOGRAPHY
Unpublished.

BERNARDINO FUNGAI

Siena, 1460-1516

Annunciation - Marriage of the Virgin - Dead Christ between two Angels

Panels of a Predella. Panels, 39 × 52 cm. each.

CONDITION: the small panels were very severely damaged in 1944, remaining under the rubble of a house blown up by mines in Florence. Completely restored by G. Marchig. PROVENANCE: unknown.

"... Fungai was a distressingly unequal painter: at times he was distinguished and imaginative, using a technique and notation both original and effective, but again he became as dull and heavy as, say, Giovanni Santi at his lowest level. Nor can it be a mere accident that there have remained to us more narrative paintings of the cassone kind by him than by any other of his Sienese contemporaries. In these he is always vivid, always amusing, and decorative."

B. BERENSON, *Homeless Pictures - The Fifteenth Century Sienese* (from the author's original manuscript, p. 37).

Fungai's sweet, somewhat affected style, a weakening of Matteo di Giovanni's formula, together with those of Cozzarelli and Girolamo di Benvenuto, achieves in this predella a tender, anecdotal grace.

BIBLIOGRAPHY

B. BERENSON: *The Central Italian Painters of the Renaissance*, New York-London, G. P. Putnam's Sons 1909, p. 171 - F. MASON PERKINS: *Pitture Senesi Poco Conosciute*, in «La Diana», VI, 1931, p. 32 (republished in «Pitture Senesi», Siena, 1933, p. 65) - B. BERENSON: 1932, p. 211 - B. BERENSON: 1936, p. 182 - R. VAN MARLE: vol. XVI, 1937, p. 467 («*Annunciation*») e p. 484 («*Sposalizio*» and «*Dead Christ with two Angels*») - P. BACCI: *Bernardino Fungai Pittore Senese*, Siena, 1947, p. 6.

C

FRANCESCO GRANACCI

Florence, 1477-1543

Saint before an idol - Saint at the stake

Two altar panels, 37 × 54 cm. each.

CONDITION: severely damaged under the rubble of a house in Florence blown up by mines in 1944. Completely restored by G. Marchig. PROVENANCE: acquired in New York.

" Francesco Granacci, like Ridolfo [Ghirlandajo] whom he influenced so largely, was active chiefly in the sixteenth century; yet his manner, despite his pilferings from such of his younger contemporaries as Pontormo, was so much either that of a Quattrocentist pure and simple, or of one not really developing a newer style, but simply declining upon the older, that we shall do best to study him here, in connection with his masters [David and Domenico] the Ghirlandajo. Was Ghirlandajo, however, his only master? His paintings leave the question undecided for in them, from the first, Granacci betrays eclectic tendencies ... "

B. BERENSON, The Drawings of the Florentine Painters, London, 1903, p. 122.

These works were part of the group of panels which Granacci painted for the altar designed by Michelangelo, according to Vasari, for the Convent of St. Apollonia. Six small paintings depicting scenes from the lives and martyrdoms of St. Agnes, St. Catherine, St. Apollonia, St. Lucy (whose relics were kept in the Church), and another two unknown Saints (Nos. 8690, 91, 92, 93, 94, 95) are at the Accademia in Florence, together with two panels " with three angels each bearing lilies " (Milanese). The Munich Pinokathek has four panels coming from *St. Apollonia*, picturing the *Magdalen*, *St. Apollonia*, *St. Jerome* and *St. John the Baptist* (each 126 × 62 cm., numbered from 1065 to 1068). Paatz, who does not consider the Munich panels as relating to the altar, thinks that its central painting was Granacci's *Assumption*, No. 1596 of the Uffizi. The small pictures of the Florence Accademia were taken there from the Convent of St. Apollonia in 1810. At that time there were eight, but a ninth scene is mentioned which was burned in the 18th C. In 1813, two of the eight small paintings were given up in an exchange with the dealer Angelo Volpini; perhaps these are the panels in the Berenson collection.

Professor Zeri advises me that another small painting of the series (hence, originally composed of ten pieces) was formerly part of Lord Kinnaird's collection at Rossie Priory, Inchture, Pertshire, and is currently in a New York collection. He believes that the work had already been removed from St. Apollonia before the Napoleonic suppressions.

The problem of reassembling the altar which Vasari refers to, is very difficult. Freedberg, who stresses the influence of Michelangelo in the series of paintings, maintains that the Munich saints were part of the group. Zeri, who has carried on researches with regard to this problem and who has received ample documentation from Dr. Procacci, does not believe that the Uffizi *Assumption* was the central part of the altar. He puts forward the theory that the small panels (eight of which arrived at the Accademia joined together into two large panels) were originally, despite Vasari's assertion, reliquary closet doors, which agrees with the description in the inventory of the Volpini exchange: " due sportelli di armadio per reliquie... molto patiti."

BIBLIOGRAPHY

G. VASARI: *Le Vite*, (ed. G. Milanesi), 1906, vol. V, p. 344 and note 2 - B. BERENSON: 1932, p. 266 - B. BERENSON: 1936, p. 229 - U. PROCACCI: *La R. Galleria dell'Accademia di Firenze*, Rome, 1936, p. 50 - W. PAATZ: *Die Kirchen von Florenz*, Frankfurt am Main, 1940, vol. I, pp. 216, 223-24 note - *Catalogue: Alte Pinakothek*, Munich, 1958, p. 44 - S. J. FREEDBERG: *Painting of the High Renaissance in Rome and Florence*, Cambridge (USA), 1961, I. pp. 492 ff.

Half-bust portrait of a man

Panel, 53 × 45 cm.

CONDITION: wormholes in the panel; the pigment is dirty and covered with oxidized varnish. PROVENANCE: unknown.

Berenson suggested a doubtful attribution to V. Pagani. Despite the oxidation of the colours, the portrait reveals notable qualities, and seems derived from the style of Alvise Vivarini.

BIBLIOGRAPHY
Unpublished.

INDEX OF PAINTERS and PLATE NUMBERS

Printing completed

ARTI GRAFICHE RICORDI S.p.A. - MILANO

June 30,[th] 1964